Math Mammoth
Grade 2-B Worktext

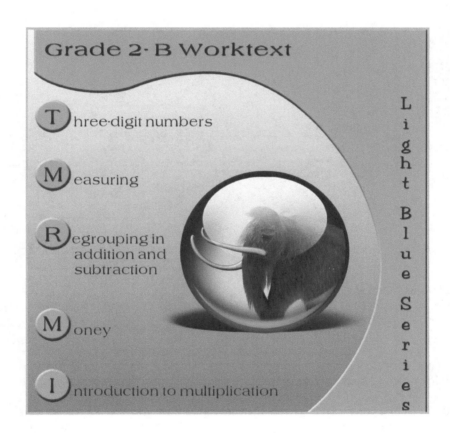

Grade 2·B Worktext

Three-digit numbers

Measuring

Regrouping in addition and subtraction

Money

Introduction to multiplication

Light Blue Series

By Maria Miller

Contents

Chapter 8: Regrouping in Addition and Subtraction

Chapter 9: Money

Chapter 10: Exploring Multiplication

Foreword

Math Mammoth Grade 2 comprises a complete math curriculum for the second grade mathematics studies. The curriculum meets and exceeds the Common Core standards.

The main areas of study for second grade are:

1. Understanding of the base-ten system within 1000. This includes place value with three-digit numbers, skip-counting in fives, tens, and multiples of hundreds, tens, and ones (within 1000) (chapters 6 and 8);

2. Develop fluency with addition and subtraction, including solving word problems, regrouping in addition, and regrouping in subtraction (chapters 1, 3, 4, and 8);

3. Using standard units of measure (chapter 7);

4. Describing and analyzing shapes (chapter 5).

Additional topics we study are time, money, introduction to multiplication, and bar graphs and picture graphs.

This book, 2-B, covers three-digit numbers (chapter 6), measuring (chapter 7), regrouping in addition and subtraction (chapter 8), counting coins (chapter 9), and an introduction to multiplication (chapter 10). The rest of the topics are covered in the 2-A student worktext.

Some important points to keep in mind when using the curriculum:

- These two books (parts A and B) are like a "framework", but you still have a lot of liberty in planning your child's studies. While addition and subtraction topics are best studied in the order they are presented, feel free to go through the sections on shapes, measurement, clock, and money in any order you like.

  This is especially advisable if your child is either "stuck" or is perhaps getting bored with some particular topic. Sometimes the concept the child was stuck on can become clear after a break from the topic.

- Math Mammoth is mastery-based, which means it concentrates on a few major topics at a time, in order to study them in depth. However, you can still use it in a *spiral* manner, if you prefer. Simply have your child study in 2-3 chapters simultaneously. This type of flexible use of the curriculum enables you to truly individualize the instruction for your child.

- Don't automatically assign all the exercises. Use your judgment, trying to assign just enough for your child's needs. You can use the skipped exercises later for review. For most children, I recommend to start out by assigning about half of the available exercises. Adjust as necessary.

- For review, the curriculum includes a worksheet maker (Internet access required), mixed review lessons, additional cumulative review lessons, and the word problems continually require usage of past concepts. Please see more information about review (and other topics) in the FAQ at **https://www.mathmammoth.com/faq-lightblue.php**

I heartily recommend that you view the full user guide for your grade level, available at **https://www.mathmammoth.com/userguides/**

Lastly, you can find free videos matched to the curriculum at **https://www.mathmammoth.com/videos/**

I wish you success in teaching math!

Maria Miller, the author

Chapter 6: Three-Digit Numbers
Introduction

This sixth chapter of *Math Mammoth Grade 2* deals with numbers up to one thousand.

The first three lessons provide the basis for understanding three-digit numbers and place value. The lessons use a visual model of hundred-flats, ten-pillars, and one-cubes. If you prefer, you can use manipulatives instead (base ten blocks). We also study three-digit numbers on a number line, and in the following lesson, *Forming Numbers—and Breaking Them Apart*, children practice writing numbers in expanded form (as a sum of their "parts": hundreds, tens, and ones).

Next, it is time to study *Skip-Counting by Tens*, and soon also by twos and fives. Then we compare and order three-digit numbers.

After this, it is time for some mental math. First, we study *Adding and Subtracting Whole Hundreds* mentally. Children practice completing the next hundred (e.g. 260 + ____ = 300) and add and subtract whole tens mentally. Along the way, they also solve word problems and other types of problems.

The chapter ends with some bar graphs and pictographs, which provide a nice application for the recently learned three-digit numbers.

I also want to include a friendly reminder here concerning the free videos matching the curriculum at **https://www.mathmammoth.com/videos/** (choose 2nd grade). Also, don't automatically assign all the problems and exercises, but use your judgment. Many children can learn these topics perfectly fine by doing about half of the exercises.

The Lessons

Helpful Resources on the Internet

Scan me

You can also access this list of links at **https://l.mathmammoth.com/gr2ch6**

Base Ten Blocks
Click "Next problem" to get a number to make with the blocks. You can adjust the number of columns to make the problem easier or more challenging.
https://www.hoodamath.com/games/basetenblocks.html

Place Value Crossword Puzzle
Fill in the puzzle by answering the questions.
https://www.free-training-tutorial.com/word-games/crossword-puzzles-place-value-3.html

Mountains Hot Air Balloons
Practice combining numbers to make new ones. With a correct answer, the hot air balloon is sent into the air!
https://www.free-training-tutorial.com/place-value/long-equations.html

Sea Life - Place Value Expanded Form
Practice adding in expanded form. With each correct answer, you add beautiful fish, sea shells, coral, and more to the sea floor.
https://www.free-training-tutorial.com/place-value/sealife/sl-expanded-form.html

Cookie Dough
Either spell the number in words or write the digits.
https://www.funbrain.com/games/cookie-dough-spell-the-numbers

Placing Numbers on a Number Line
Choose one type of number line or several for more of a challenge. Work quickly to get more time, build your score and climb up the leader board. Click "full screen", then choose "Between multiples of 100".
https://mathsframe.co.uk/en/resources/resource/37/placing_numbers_on_a_number_line

Sequences
Find the correct number in a skip-counting sequence. Click "Full screen", then choose whole numbers.
https://mathsframe.co.uk/en/resources/resource/42/sequences

Number Sequences
Skip-counting practice with lots of options – think the answer, then reveal it.
https://www.topmarks.co.uk/Flash.aspx?f=NumberSequences

COMPARING

Coconut Ordering
Click on the coconuts in order from the smallest value to the largest. Choose "Ordering Numbers", 'Up to 1,000".
https://www.topmarks.co.uk/ordering-and-sequencing/coconut-ordering

Balancing Calculations
Find the missing number to balance the calculations. Choose "Add 3 Digit Number and Hundreds".
https://mathsframe.co.uk/en/resources/resource/587/Balancing-Calculations

Make a Greater Number
Can you beat the computer? Make a 3-digit number with a greater value by choosing the place for each digit. Note: Loads very slowly in Chrome, and doesn't work in Firefox.
https://www.learnalberta.ca/content/me3us/flash/lessonLauncher.html?lesson=lessons/05/m3_05_00_x.swf

ADDITION AND SUBTRACTION

Addition Practice—Expanded Form
Practice adding in expanded form with this interactive online exercise.
https://www.mathmammoth.com/practice/place-value#mode=write-number&max-digits=3&question-number=10

Missing Number Addition Practice
Find the missing number in each addition problem.
https://www.mathmammoth.com/practice/place-value#mode=missing-part&max-digits=3&question-number=10

Mostly Postie
Drag the parcel onto the scales, then enter the value shown to deliver your letter or parcel. Practice counting in 10s and 100s.
https://www.ictgames.com/mobilePage/mostlyPostie/index.html

Adding/Subtracting Multiples of 100
Answer as many questions as you can in this online quiz.
http://www.snappymaths.com/addsub/addsubp10/interactive/addsubmult100/addsubmult100.htm

Close Call Addition Card Game (Page 5 of PDF file)
Create sums as close to 100 as you can without going over.
https://bit.ly/dice-card-games

Addition Quiz – Multiples of Ten
Practice your addition skills with this online quiz.
https://www.thatquiz.org/tq-1/?-jkg01-l1i-p0

Subtracting Multiples of 10 from 3-Digit Numbers
Answer as many questions as you can in this online quiz.
http://www.snappymaths.com/addsub/addsubp10/interactive/subm10f3dm10int/subm10f3dm10int.htm

Add 10s and 100s Mentally
Practice mental addition of 2-digit and 3-digit numbers with this interactive online exercise.
https://www.khanacademy.org/math/arithmetic-home/addition-subtraction/add-ones-tens-hundreds/e/add-within-1000--level-1

Add and Subtract on a Number Line
Practice adding and subtracting numbers using a number line. All numbers are less than 1,000.
https://bit.ly/add-subtract-number-line

GRAPHS

Thatquiz.org Quiz for Graphs
A 10-question quiz involving bar graphs and pictographs.
https://www.thatquiz.org/tq-5/?-j40v0h-l1-p0

Math 3: Under the Sea Data Collecting Activity
Practice gathering, organizing, and displaying data in this interactive online activity. Note: Loads slowly in Chrome, and doesn't work in Firefox.
https://www.learnalberta.ca/content/me3us/flash/lessonLauncher.html?lesson=lessons/15/m3_15_00_x.swf

Reading Bar Charts Activity
Practices reading bar charts with vertical or horizontal bars.
https://mathsframe.co.uk/en/resources/resource/51/bar_charts

Three-Digit Numbers

Ten ones make a ten: Ten ten-pillars make ONE HUNDRED:

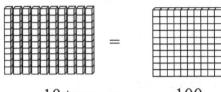

10 ones = 10   10 tens =   100

Write hundreds, tens, and ones in their own columns:

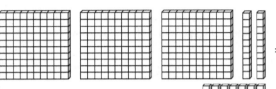

three hundred twenty-seven

hund-reds	tens	ones
3	2	7

1. Count the ones, tens, and hundreds, and fill in the missing parts.

a. one hundred one	**b.** one hundred six	**c.** one hundred eleven	**d.** one hundred thirteen
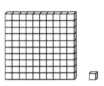	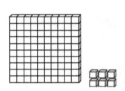	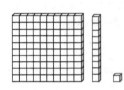	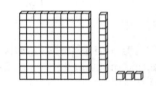

hundreds	tens	ones
1	0	1

hundreds	tens	ones

hundreds	tens	ones
1	1	1

hundreds	tens	ones

e. one hundred twenty	**f.** one hundred twenty-five	**g.** one hundred fifty	**h.** one hundred sixty-two
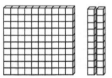	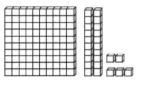	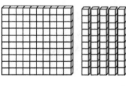	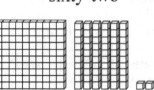

hundreds	tens	ones

hundreds	tens	ones

hundreds	tens	ones

hundreds	tens	ones

2. Count the ones, tens, and hundreds, and fill in the missing parts.

a. _two hundred_ _____ _four_ _____

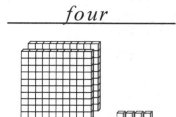

hundreds	tens	ones
2	0	4

b. _two hundred_ _____ _thirteen_ _____

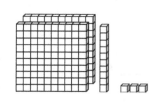

hundreds	tens	ones

c. _____ _____

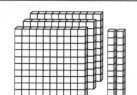

hundreds	tens	ones

d. _____ _____

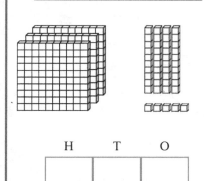

H	T	O

e. _____ _____

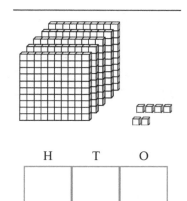

H	T	O

f. _____ _____

H	T	O

g. _____

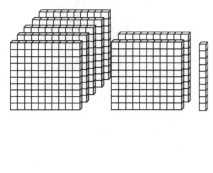

H	T	O

h. _Ten hundreds = One thousand_

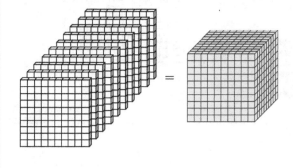

Th	H	T	O
1	0	0	0

3. Write a sum of the hundreds, tens, and ones shown in the picture.
   Also write the number.

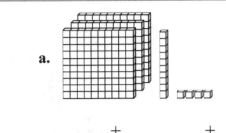

a.

_____ + _____ + _____

H	T	O

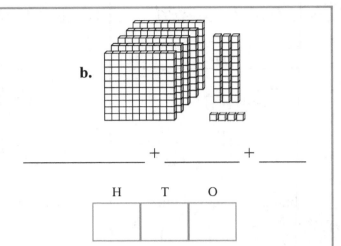

b.

_____ + _____ + _____

H	T	O

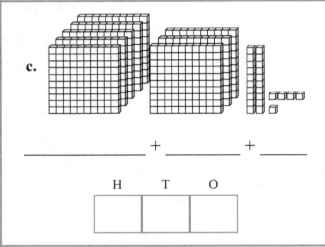

c.

_____ + _____ + _____

H	T	O

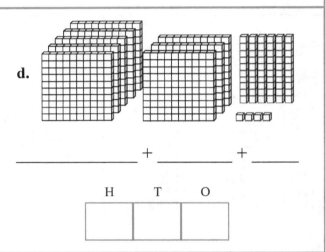

d.

_____ + _____ + _____

H	T	O

Notice: There are NO ones.
Write a zero for ones in the sum.

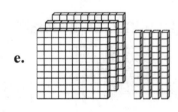

e.

_____ + _____ + _0_

H	T	O

Notice: There are NO tens.
Write a zero for tens in the sum.

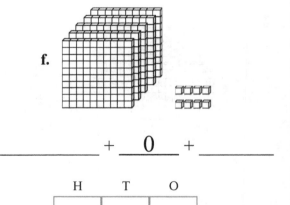

f.

_____ + _0_ + _____

H	T	O

12

4. Match the numbers, number names, and the sums to the correct pictures.

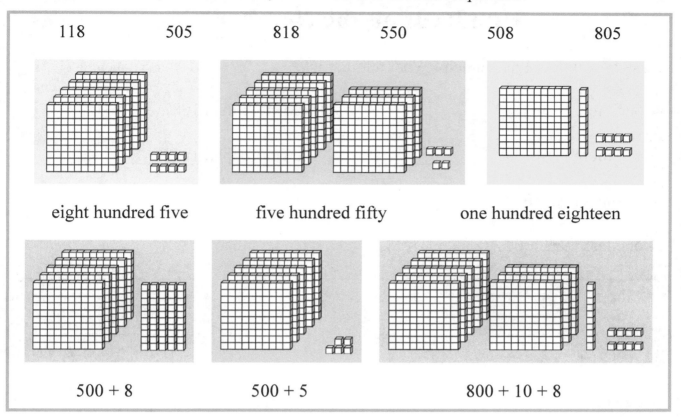

118   505   818   550   508   805

eight hundred five   five hundred fifty   one hundred eighteen

500 + 8   500 + 5   800 + 10 + 8

5. The dots are ones, the pillars are tens. Group together 10 ten-pillars to make a hundred.

a.

235

b.

_____

c.

_____

d.

_____

How many tens are in a thousand?

13

Hundreds on the Number Line

1. Use the number lines to help. What number is...

a. one more than 118? _____

one more than 134? _____

one less than 103? _____

one less than 130? _____

b. ten more than 108? _____

ten more than 125? _____

ten less than 140? _____

ten less than 127? _____

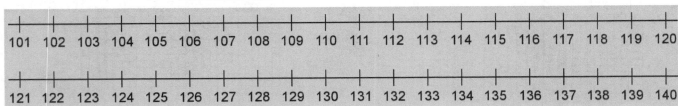

c. two more than 193? _____

two more than 178? _____

two less than 170? _____

two less than 190? _____

d. ten more than 164? _____

ten more than 188? _____

ten less than 200? _____

ten less than 177? _____

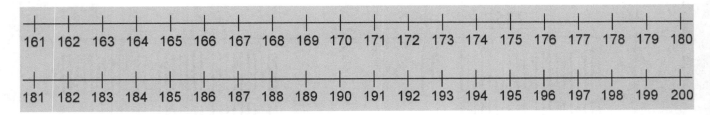

2. Find the differences.

a. The difference of 165 and 171	**b.** The difference of 185 and 192
_____	_____
c. The difference of 200 and 191	**d.** The difference of 140 and 124
_____	_____

3. Fill in the numbers for these number lines.

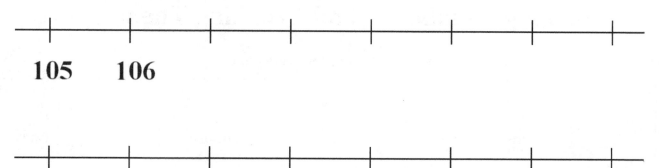

105   **106**

196   **197**

4. Mark on the number line: 244, 256, 301, 308, 299, 245, 255, 262, 223, 211.

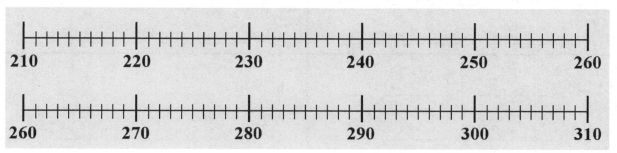

5. **Notice:** This number line does NOT have the little tick marks between the whole tens. Mark these numbers approximately on the number line: 945, 902, 996, 928, 895.

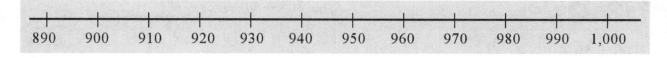

890   900   910   920   930   940   950   960   970   980   990   1,000

6. **a.** Draw a number line from 400 to 450. Only write the numbers below the whole tens tick marks.

b. Mark on your number line these numbers: 413, 402, 436, 415, 439.

Forming Numbers—and Breaking Them Apart

1. Break these numbers into their hundreds, tens, and ones.

a. 276	**b.** 867
= ____ hundreds ____ tens ____ ones	= ____ hundreds ____ tens ____ ones
= 200 + 70 + 6	= 800 + _____ + _____
c. 350	**d.** 707
= ____ hundreds ____ tens ____ ones	= ____ hundreds ____ tens ____ ones
= _____ + _____ + ____	= _____ + _____ + ____
e. 409 = _____ + _____ + ____	**h.** 940 = _____ + _____ + ____
f. 601 = _____ + _____ + ____	**i.** 383 = _____ + _____ + ____
g. 558 = _____ + _____ + ____	**j.** 627 = _____ + _____ + ____

2. These numbers have been "broken down." Collect the parts and write the numbers.

a. 700 + 30 + 3 = _____	**b.** 200 + 40 + 5 = _____
100 + 50 = _____	400 + 7 = _____

3. These numbers have been "broken down." Again, collect the parts and write them as numbers. This time, the parts are in scrambled order, so be careful!

a. 20 + 700 + 8 = _____	**b.** 50 + 600 = _____
30 + 3 + 900 = _____	1 + 800 = _____
c. 2 ones 1 hundred 4 tens = _____	**d.** 3 hundreds 3 tens = _____
8 tens 0 ones 1 hundred = _____	9 ones 5 hundreds = _____

4. Find out what number the triangle represents, but don't write the number inside the triangle. Write it on the empty line.

a. $900 + 20 + 4 = \triangle$

$\triangle$ is _____

b. $60 + 400 = \triangle$

$\triangle$ is _____

c. $7 + 100 = \triangle$

$\triangle =$ _____

5. One of the "parts" for the numbers is missing. Find out what number the triangle represents.

a. $700 + \triangle + 5 = 735$

$\triangle =$ _____

b. $400 + 40 + \triangle = 449$

$\triangle =$ _____

c. $7 + \triangle + 90 = 297$

$\triangle =$ _____

6. Find out what number the triangle represents. Actually, you are solving equations!

a. $7 + \triangle = 70$

$\triangle =$ _____

b. $7 - \triangle = 0$

$\triangle =$ _____

c. $\triangle - 7 = 7$

$\triangle =$ _____

7. Write your own "triangle problems" (equations), and let a friend solve them.

a.

$\triangle =$ _____

b.

$\triangle =$ _____

c.

$\triangle =$ _____

Find what number the triangle represents!

(Note, the problem $12 - \triangle - \triangle = 2$ does not have two different numbers as the $\triangle$. In other words, the triangle represents the same number both times.)

 Puzzle Corner

a. $12 - \triangle - \triangle = 2$

$\triangle =$ _____

b. $19 - \triangle - \triangle = 7$

$\triangle =$ _____

c. $120 - \triangle - \triangle = 60$

$\triangle =$ _____

Skip-Counting by Tens

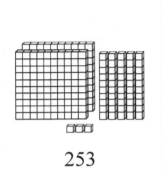

253

What number is <u>10 more</u> than 253?

Imagine drawing one more ten-pillar in the picture. We would get 263.

Or, you can think this way: the tens digit "5" in 2<u>5</u>3 changes to "6":   2<u>5</u>3 + 10 = 2<u>6</u>3.

What number is <u>ten less</u> than 253?

Imagine taking away one ten-pillar from the picture. We would have 243.

In the subtraction below, the tens digit "5" changes to "4". 2<u>5</u>3 − 10 = 2<u>4</u>3.

1. Add or subtract whole tens. You can draw more for the picture, or take away from the picture, to help you!

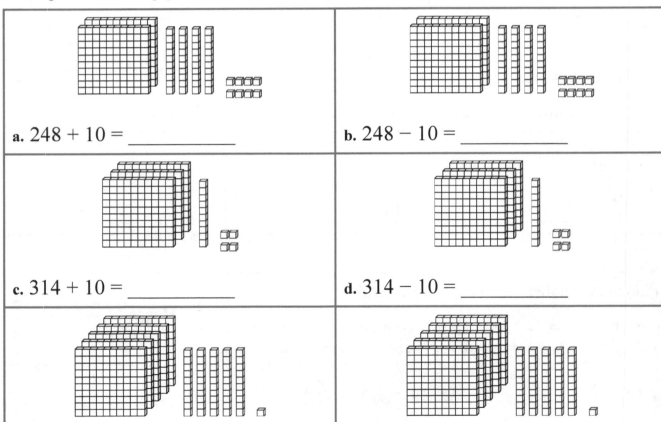

a. 248 + 10 = _____

b. 248 − 10 = _____

c. 314 + 10 = _____

d. 314 − 10 = _____

e. 551 + 20 = _____

f. 551 − 20 = _____

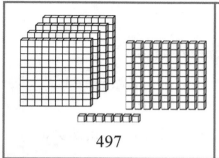

497

What number is <u>ten more</u> than 497?

Draw one more ten-pillar. Now you have 10 ten-pillars! Those make <u>a new hundred</u>. Circle that new hundred.

So, now you have FIVE hundreds, zero tens, and 7 ones.

$$497 + 10 = 507$$

Trick: Look at the two digits formed by the hundreds and tens digits—the "49" in 497. That is actually how many tens you have, if you also count the tens in the 4 hundreds.

When we add one ten to 49 tens, we of course get 50 tens. It is like the digit-pair "49" in 497 changing to "50." So, we get 507.

$$\underline{49}7 + 10 = \underline{50}7$$

2. Add whole tens. Draw more in the picture to help. Circle any new hundreds you get.

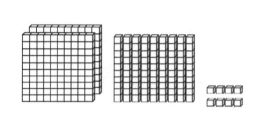

a. 298 + 10 = _____

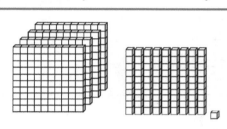

b. 491 + 10 = _____

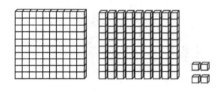

c. 194 + 10 = _____

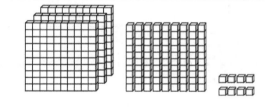

d. 398 + 10 = _____

3. Skip-count by tens.

a. 704, 714, _____, _____, _____, _____, _____, _____

b. 331, 341, _____, _____, _____, _____, _____, _____

c. 467, 477, _____, _____, _____, _____, _____, _____

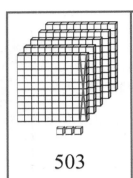

What number is <u>ten less</u> than 503?

Try to take away one ten-pillar—but there aren't any!

You will have to take away one ten from one of the hundreds. That ten is marked out with a red "x" in the picture.

This means you will have left four hundreds, nine tens, and also the three little ones: 5<u>0</u>3 − 10 = 4<u>9</u>3

503

Trick: Look at the two digits formed by the hundreds and tens digits—the "50" in 503. That is how many tens you actually have (50), if you count the tens in the 5 hundreds. When we subtract a ten from those 50 tens, we get 49 tens. It means the digit-pair "50" changes to "49." So, we get 493:   **50**3 − 10 = **49**3

4. Subtract a ten. Cross out a ten in the picture to help.

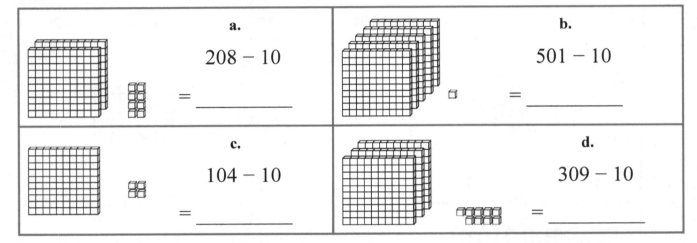

a.

$208 - 10$

= _____

b.

$501 - 10$

= _____

c.

$104 - 10$

= _____

d.

$309 - 10$

= _____

5. Write the number that is 10 less and 10 more than the given number.

a. ___*610*___, 620, ___*630*___   b. _____, 698, _____

c. _____, 710, _____   d. _____, 606, _____

e. _____, 129, _____   f. _____, 505, _____

6. Skip-count by tens backwards.

a. 731, 721, _____, _____, _____, _____, _____, _____

b. _____, _____, _____, 920, 910, _____, _____, _____

More Skip-Counting

1. Fill in the number chart from 971 till 1000.

971	972								
981	982								

2. Count by fives. The number chart can help for some of these. You can also do it orally.

a. 960, 965, 970, _____, _____, _____, _____, _____

b. 435, 440, _____, _____, _____, _____, _____, _____

c. _____, _____, _____, _____, _____, _____, 400, 405

3. Count by twos. The number chart can help. You can also do it orally.

a. 968, 970, _____, _____, _____, _____, _____, _____

b. _____, _____, _____, _____, _____, _____, 502, 504

c. 479, 481, _____, _____, _____, _____, _____, _____

4. Find a number that is <u>10 less</u> than the number shown in the picture.

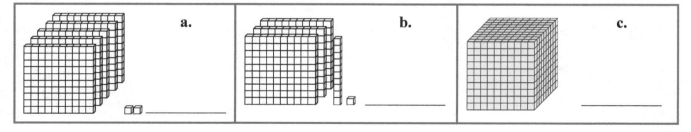

5. This number chart is filled in counting by tens. You don't have to fill it in, but you may. Now a CHALLENGE: What will be the LAST number on the chart?

_____ Try to figure this out *without* filling it in completely!

710	720	730							
810									

6. Write the numbers before and after the given number (one less and one more).

a. _____, 700, _____   b. _____, 129, _____

c. _____, 450, _____   d. _____, 801, _____

e. _____, 671, _____   f. _____, 999, _____

7. Count by tens, fives, and twos. You can also do this orally with your teacher.

a. 748, 758, _____, _____, _____, _____, _____

b. _____, _____, _____, 423, 433, _____, _____

c. 480, 485, _____, _____, _____, _____, _____

d. _____, _____, _____, _____, _____, 720, 725

e. _____, _____, _____, _____, _____, 995, 1,000

f. _____, _____, _____, 506, 508, _____, _____

g. 695, 697, _____, _____, _____, _____, _____

h. _____, _____, _____, _____, _____, 431, 433

Which Number Is Greater?

1. Can you tell which number is more? Try! Write < or > between the numbers.

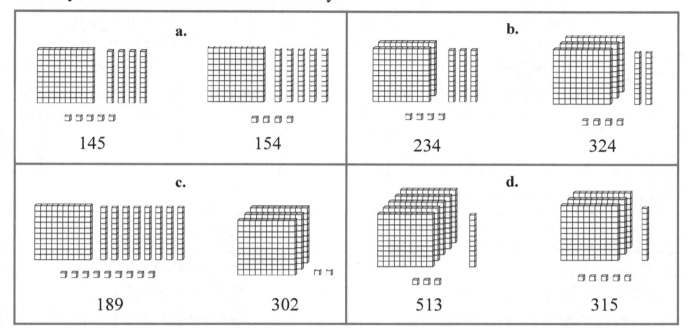

a.		b.	
145	154	234	324

c.		d.	
189	302	513	315

Learn the new symbols:

☐ = 100, | = 10, and . = 1.   ☐ ‖ .... = 124   ☐ ☐ ‖‖‖ = 240

2. Draw the symbols ☐ , | , and . for the numbers. Then compare and write < or > .

a. 120	130	**b.** 240	420
c. 305	503	**d.** 453	534

To compare three-digit numbers:

1. First check if one number has more **hundreds** than the other.
   For example, 652 < 701, because 701 has more hundreds than 652.

2. If the numbers have the same amount of hundreds, then check the **tens**.
   For example, 652 > 639 because though both have six hundreds, 652 has more tens than 639.

3. If the numbers have the same amount of hundreds AND the same amount of tens, then look at the **ones**. For example, 652 < 655 because though both have six hundreds and five tens, 655 has more **ones**.

Remember, the open end (open mouth) of the symbols < and > ALWAYS opens towards the bigger number.

3. Find the biggest number in each set!

a. 259, 592, 295	**b.** 470, 774, 747	**c.** 409, 944, 949	**d.** 506, 605, 505
e. 911, 119, 191	**f.** 482, 382, 284	**g.** 334, 433, 403	**h.** 208, 820, 802

4. Write either < or > in between the numbers.

a. 159 < 300	**b.** 122 100	**c.** 320 328	**d.** 212 284
e. 200 190	**f.** 600 860	**g.** 456 465	**h.** 711 599
i. 780 500	**j.** 107 700	**k.** 566 850	**l.** 840 480

5. Arrange the three numbers in order.

a. 140, 156, 149 *140 < 149 < 156*	**b.** 357, 573, 750
c. 239, 286, 133	**d.** 670, 766, 676

6. Mark the numbers on the number line: 513, 530, 489, 468, 596, 606, 560, 466, 506, 516

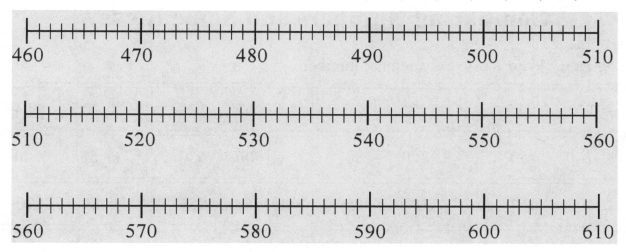

7. Find a number to write on the empty line. There are many possibilities!

   a. 140 < _____ < 149

   b. 267 < _____ < 804

   c. 279 < _____ < 290

   d. 304 < _____ < 310

8. Find your way through the maze! The rules are: you can move either left, right, or down, provided that the number following is BIGGER than the number in the square you are in.

100	121	127	133	167	189	200	214	212	398
145	166	134	135	120	230	212	256	347	405
156	167	137	156	155	226	356	378	380	407
632	234	138	246	267	278	476	477	450	417
432	256	200	250	245	300	355	487	478	456
355	253	289	244	305	303	570	569	490	453
361	385	377	367	356	301	537	566	505	498
689	654	390	480	478	488	675	507	508	689
654	543	489	488	483	577	589	609	504	769
723	566	570	589	578	734	631	616	789	**1000**

Comparing Numbers and Some Review

1. Compare. Write < or > between the numbers.

a. 150 < 515	**b.** 22 120	**c.** 307 320	**d.** 412 284
e. 240 750	**f.** 860 680	**g.** 406 620	**h.** 558 540
i. 605 450	**j.** 107 705	**k.** 566 856	**l.** 890 870

2. Compare the sums and write < , > , or = .

    a. 300 + 60 + 5 ☐ 365

    b. 300 + 4 ☐ 300 + 40

    c. 200 + 60 + 4 ☐ 60 + 4 + 200

    d. 300 + 5 ☐ 400 + 1

    e. 4 + 900 + 8 ☐ 500 + 90 + 8

    f. 100 + 8 ☐ 10 + 8

    g. 800 + 70 + 2 ☐ 700 + 80 + 7

    h. 90 + 8 ☐ 8 + 900

3. Mark the numbers on the number line: 810, 725, 799, 802, 843, 795, 801, 766, 729

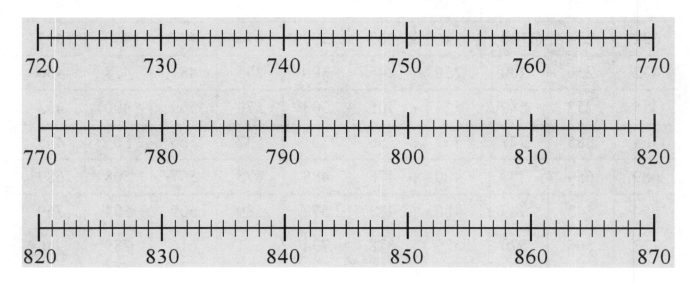

4. Arrange the numbers in order and write in boxes the corresponding letters.

What is white and hiding in a bush?

H	Y	S	A	S	H	E	K	M	K	L	I	A
770	455	105	77	757	350	957	803	503	707	517	515	777

[ ]   [ ] [ ] [ ]

____ < ____ < ____ < ____ <

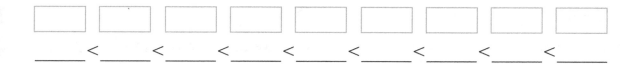

[ ] [ ] [ ] [ ] [ ] [ ] [ ] [ ] [ ]

____ < ____ < ____ < ____ < ____ < ____ < ____ < ____ < ____

5. What are these broken down numbers?

a. $6 + 700 = $ _____	b. $40 + 100 + 1 = $ _____
$600 + 70 = $ _____	$1 + 400 + 10 = $ _____

6. Write a number on each empty line so that the comparisons are true.
   For some problems there are many possible answers.

a. $750 + $ _____ $>$ 757	b. 645 $=$ $600 + 5 + $ _____
c. $200 + $ _____ $>$ $200 + 60 + 4$	d. 278 $>$ _____ $+ 5$
e. _____ $+ 4$ $<$ $900 + 8$	f. $100 + 8$ $<$ _____ $+ 90$

	**a.** It is the same whether you read it from left to right or from right to left. It is less than 100, but more than 92.
b. The digits of this number add up to nine. It is more than 50 but less than 60.	**c.** This number is between 30 and 40. If you count by tens from it, you will eventually get to 78.

27

7. Learning game - make numbers with dominoes!

You will need: paper, pencils, and a standard set of dominoes (from zero-zero to six-six), from which you take away six-six, five-five, and five-six. Optionally for each player: you need three paper plates. Write on their top part the words: Hundreds, Tens, Ones. This game is for two to six people.

Goal: In this game, you build a number with dominoes so that one (or two) dominoes make up the hundreds digit, one (or two) dominoes make up the tens digit, and one (or two) dominoes make up the ones digit. You just add up the dots in the domino(es) to get the digit. The goal is to build your number as close to a given target number as possible. The player who gets closest to the target number wins.

Rules: The players determine who starts. The dominoes are upside down in front of the players. The game leader announces a target number, which is any whole hundred from 300 to 900. Then, each player takes three dominoes randomly, and makes his number out of them. Each player's dominoes are visible to the others.

Then everyone will get a chance to take ONE more domino, if they wish (this is not mandatory). The player can add that domino to any of the digits (ones, tens, or hundreds). After that, the numbers are checked, and whoever gets the closest number to the target number, wins.

For example, if you get the dominoes four-three, two-two, and one-four, it means you can use the digits seven, four, and five. Let's say the target number is 600, so you build your number to be 547. Then, you choose to pick up one more domino, which ends up being one-three. So you need to add four to one of your digits. You add it to your tens, getting 587.

Here is another example. If you have built the number 789 and you pick a new domino six-three, then you need to add nine to one of your digits. But that will make them "spill over" to the next place value. So either you add nine to your ones, resulting in 789 + 9 = 798, or you add nine tens, resulting in 789 + 90 = 879, or you add nine hundreds, resulting in 789 + 900 = 1689.

Variation 1: In each round, you can choose to give the losers as many points as they were away from the target number, and continue playing till someone reaches a pre-determined "losing" number, such as 1,000.

Variation 2: You can let each player either add *or subtract* the additional domino from any of the place values. For example, if you have built 328 and you pick one-one, you could subtract two from your tens, leaving you 308.

Add and Subtract Whole Hundreds

1. A dot is one, a stick is a ten, and a square is a hundred. Write the addition sentences.
   Add in columns as well. Hundreds will go in their own column!

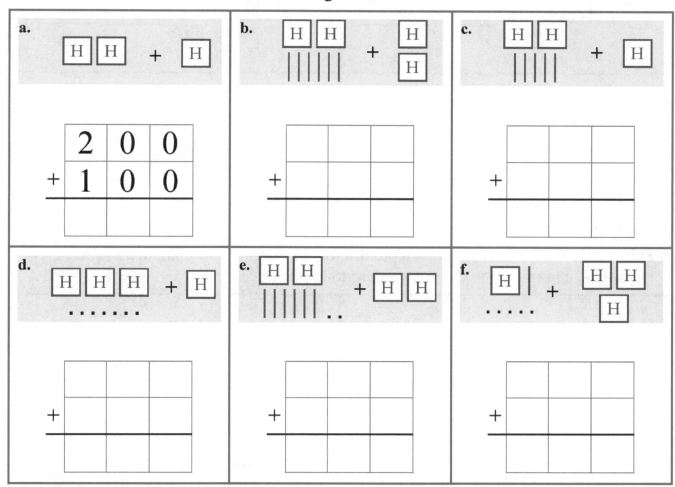

$$\underline{5}14 + \underline{2}00 = ??$$

Add mentally 500 and 200, or the whole hundreds.
That is 700. The answer is 714.

Only the hundreds digit will change! The "14" does not change.

2. Add whole hundreds.

a.	b.	c.
615 + 200 = _____	409 + 400 = _____	722 + 200 = _____
278 + 300 = _____	563 + 100 = _____	194 + 500 = _____

3. Cross out what needs subtracted from the pictures. Subtract in columns as well.

a. Cross out 100.

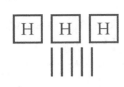

$$\begin{array}{r} 4\ 0\ 0 \\ -\ 1\ 0\ 0 \\ \hline \end{array}$$

b. Cross out 100.

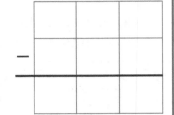

c. Cross out 500.

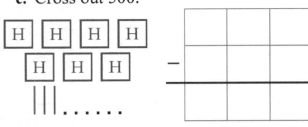

d. Cross out 400.

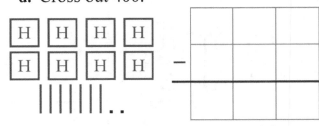

4. Subtract. To help, you can draw a picture for the number using hundred-squares, ten-sticks, and one-dots. Or, you can use manipulatives.

a. $507 - 200 =$ _____	**b.** $590 - 400 =$ _____
c. $345 - 200 =$ _____	**d.** $451 - 300 =$ _____

$\underline{7}38 - \underline{4}00 = ??$

Subtract mentally 700 and 400, or the whole hundreds. That is 300. The answer is 338.

Only the hundreds digit will change! The "38" does not change.

5. Subtract whole hundreds.

a.	b.	c.
$765 - 200 =$ _____	$802 - 400 =$ _____	$778 - 500 =$ _____
$548 - 300 =$ _____	$980 - 600 =$ _____	$994 - 900 =$ _____

Practice with Whole Hundreds

204 + 300 = 504 I am adding three hundred (300). Look at the hundreds digits. You can add 2 + 3 = 5 in the hundreds. ONLY the hundreds digit will change.	**465 − 200 = 265** I am subtracting two hundred (200). Look at the hundreds digits. You can subtract 4 − 2 = 2 in the hundreds. ONLY the hundreds digit will change.

1. Add whole hundreds.

a.	b.	c.
500 + 200 = _____	502 + 100 = _____	140 + 200 = _____
600 + 200 = _____	107 + 100 = _____	270 + 200 = _____

2. Subtract whole hundreds.

a.	b.	c.
600 − 300 = _____	670 − 100 = _____	550 − 200 = _____
400 − 300 = _____	107 − 100 = _____	706 − 200 = _____

3. In a game, you get 200 points if you answer a question correctly.
   You lose 100 points if you answer wrong.
   Cindy answered three questions right, and one wrong.
   How many points does she have now?

4. Subtract and add whole hundreds many times.

a.	b.
900 − 200 − 200 − 100 = _____	200 + 200 + 100 + 300 = _____
800 − 300 − 100 − 100 = _____	100 + 200 + 500 + 100 = _____

Ten hundreds = One thousand

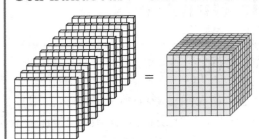

So, 1000 − 600 is the same as *10 hundreds* take away *6 hundreds*. The answer is 400.

5. Subtract from one thousand.

a. 1000 − 100 = _____ 1000 − 300 = _____	**b.** 1000 − 800 = _____ 1000 − 700 = _____
c. 1000 − 200 − 200 = _____	**d.** 1000 − 300 − 700 = _____

6. Complete one thousand.

a. 500 + _____ = 1000 600 + _____ = 1000	**b.** _____ + 700 = 1000 _____ + 900 = 1000
c. 500 + 200 + _____ = 1000 100 + 400 + _____ = 1000	**d.** 400 + _____ + 600 = 1000 _____ + 500 + 300 = 1000

7. Solve.

a. John's family is driving to Grandma's place, and from there they are going to a zoo. Dad says, "To Grandma's is 150 km, and from there to the zoo is 100 km."   How far will the family drive from their home to the zoo?
b. How far will they drive if they make a round trip? (from home to Grandma's, then to the zoo, then back to Grandma's, and back home)

8. Solve the problems.

a. One dollar is 100 cents. How many cents are in 4 dollars?  $1 = 100¢	**b.** Mary had 62¢. Her mom gave her two dollars. How many *cents* does Mary have now?
c. John had 535¢. He bought ice cream for $3. How much money does he have left?	**d.** Mia and Madison shared equally 800 marbles. How many does each girl get?
e. Daniel and Jayden live 600 meters from each other. They met at the half-way point. How far is that from each boy's house?	**f.** In a game, Anthony got 800 points. Then he lost 100 points. Then he gained 200 points more. How many points does he have now?

9. Add and subtract whole hundreds.

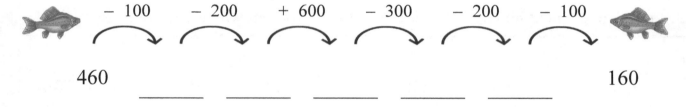

          − 100   − 200   + 600   − 300   − 200   − 100

460 _____ _____ _____ _____ _____ 160

10. How many whole hundreds were added? Find what number the triangle stands for.

a. $670 + \triangle = 770$ $\triangle = $ _____	**b.** $412 + \triangle = 812$ $\triangle = $ _____	**c.** $\triangle + 300 = 1000$ $\triangle = $ _____
d. $450 + \triangle = 850$ $\triangle = $ _____	**e.** $100 + \triangle = 1000$ $\triangle = $ _____	**f.** $\triangle + 545 = 945$ $\triangle = $ _____

33

Completing the Next Hundred

1. You need 10 ten-pillars to make a new hundred. Draw in the missing ten-pillars, and complete the next whole hundred.

H ||||| + _____ = H H **a.** 160 + _____ = 200	H H ||||| + _____ = H H H **b.** 250 + _____ = 300
H ||||||| + _____ = H H **c.** 180 + _____ = 200	H H || + _____ = H H H **d.** 220 + _____ = 300

2. Complete the next hundred. COMPARE the problems in each box.

a.	b.	c.
80 + _____ = 100	30 + _____ = 100	40 + _____ = _____
280 + _____ = 300	330 + _____ = _____	740 + _____ = _____
680 + _____ = _____	530 + _____ = _____	940 + _____ = 1000

3. Complete the next hundred. Think of a helping problem where you complete 100.

a.	b.	c.
540 + _____ = 600	250 + _____ = 300	630 + _____ = 700
(40 + _____ = 100)	(50 + _____ = 100)	(30 + _____ = 100)
d.	**e.**	**f.**
120 + _____ = _____	440 + _____ = _____	970 + _____ = _____

4. Solve each subtraction by thinking of the difference or of the "how many more" addition.

a.	b.	c.
500 − 440 = _____	800 − 710 = _____	1000 − 960 = _____
(440 + _____ = 500)	(difference of 800 and 710)	(960 + _____ = 1000)

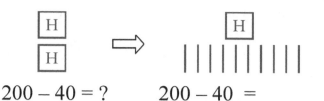

Subtract whole tens from whole hundreds

$200 - 40 = ?$ $200 - 40 = $ _____

First, break one hundred into 10 ten-pillars.

Then subtract (cross out) four ten-pillars.

5. Break down a hundred, then subtract. Draw a picture.

a. Break down a hundred. Cross out 5 tens.  $200 - 50 = $ _____	**b.** Break down a hundred. Cross out 7 tens. 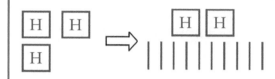 $300 - 70 = $ _____
c. Break down a hundred. Cross out 8 tens. 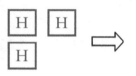 $300 - 80 = $ _____	**d.** Break down a hundred. Cross out 70. 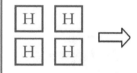 $400 - 70 = $ _____

Notice: $200 - 40 = 160$
$100 - 40 = 60$
$500 - 40 = 460$

In all cases, the ANSWER ends in "60." In the hundreds, you "go down" to the previous hundred.

6. Subtract and compare the problems!

a. $100 - 50 = $ _____	**b.** $100 - 40 = $ _____	**c.** $100 - 90 = $ _____
$300 - 50 = $ _____	$600 - 40 = $ _____	$800 - 90 = $ _____
$700 - 50 = $ _____	$200 - 40 = $ _____	$900 - 90 = $ _____

7. Solve.

a.	b.	c.
500 − 440 = _____	700 − 10 = _____	600 − 580 = _____
500 − 40 = _____	700 − 610 = _____	600 − 80 = _____

8. Solve.

a. Jane collects pretty rocks. She has 120 of them.

How many more will she need to have 200?

How many more will she need to have 300?

b. Betty had 100 pretty rocks. Then she found 30 rocks on a beach.
Then she gave 10 of those rocks to her brother.
How many rocks does she have now?

c. A large window costs $200 and a small window costs $130.
How much more does the large window cost than the small?

d. A door costs $400, and a window costs $200. Bob spent $1000 buying
one door and some windows. How many windows did he buy?

e. Dad is building a small shed. A small window for it costs $50 and a door costs
$200. Dad will buy one door and two windows. Find the total cost.

f. One week, Dad bought groceries for $200.
The next week, Mom spent $30 less than that.
How much did Mom spend for groceries?

Adding Whole Tens

1. Add whole tens.

$\boxed{H}$ ‖‖‖ and ‖‖ **a.** 160 + 30 = _____	$\boxed{H}$ $\boxed{H}$ $\boxed{H}$ ‖‖‖ and ‖ **b.** 350 + 20 = _____
$\boxed{H}$ $\boxed{H}$ ‖‖ and ‖‖ . . . . **c.** _____ + _____ = _____	$\boxed{H}$ $\boxed{H}$ $\boxed{H}$ $\boxed{H}$ ‖ and ‖‖‖‖ . . . **d.** _____ + _____ = _____

$6\underline{5}1 + \underline{2}0 = ??$

Add mentally 50 and 20, or the tens. That is 70.
The answer is then 671.

<u>Notice</u>: Only the TENS digit will change! The "6" of the hundreds does not change, nor the "1" of the ones.

2. Add whole tens. You can draw illustrations to help. Underline the tens digits to help.

a. 3$\underline{5}$0 + $\underline{3}$0 = _____	**b.** 412 + 70 = _____
c. 529 + 60 = _____	**d.** 204 + 40 = _____
e. 320 + 50 = _____	**f.** 117 + 80 = _____

3. Add. Compare the problems.

a.	b.	c.
30 + 50 = _____	71 + 20 = _____	55 + 30 = _____
230 + 50 = _____	571 + 20 = _____	255 + 30 = _____
630 + 50 = _____	871 + 20 = _____	755 + 30 = _____

4. Add whole tens. You can underline the tens to help you.

a.	b.	c.
5<u>2</u>0 + <u>2</u>0 = _____	309 + 40 = _____	722 + 50 = _____
420 + 30 = _____	553 + 20 = _____	114 + 70 = _____

5. Write the numbers in columns and add.

a.

b.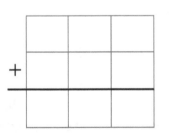

c.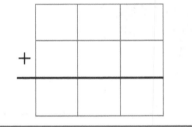

6. Count by fifties.

50	100	150		
300	350			

7. Solve the problems.

a. Roy and Rhonda collect pennies. Roy has 640 pennies now. Rhonda has 600.   How many more pennies does Roy have than Rhonda?   How many more pennies does Roy need to have 700 pennies?
b. Rhonda has 600 pennies. She shares them evenly with her little brother Jack.   How many pennies does Jack get?
c. Roy has 640 pennies. An uncle gave him 30 pennies.   How many *more* pennies does Roy still need to have 700 pennies?

8. Fill in the tens.

a.	b.	c.
$520 + \rule{1.5cm}{0.15mm} = 580$	$146 + \rule{1.5cm}{0.15mm} = 196$	$553 + \rule{1.5cm}{0.15mm} = 573$
$920 + \rule{1.5cm}{0.15mm} = 990$	$222 + \rule{1.5cm}{0.15mm} = 282$	$940 + \rule{1.5cm}{0.15mm} = 1000$

Puzzle Corner   Place either + or − signs into the squares so the number sentences are true.

$30 \; \square \; 40 \; \square \; 50 = 20$

$100 \; \square \; 40 \; \square \; 50 = 10$

$240 \; \square \; 40 \; \square \; 50 = 230$

$140 \; \square \; 80 \; \square \; 50 \; \square \; 20 = 130$

$670 \; \square \; 50 \; \square \; 20 = 640$

$930 \; \square \; 30 \; \square \; 50 = 950$

$430 \; \square \; 40 \; \square \; 50 = 520$

$200 \; \square \; 40 \; \square \; 50 \; \square \; 30 = 260$

Subtract Whole Tens

1. Cross out as many ten-pillars as the problem indicates and see what is left.

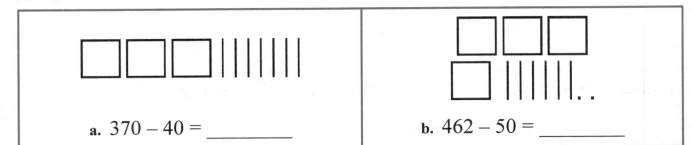

a. $370 - 40 =$ _____

b. $462 - 50 =$ _____

$7\underline{8}1 - \underline{4}0 = ??$

Subtract mentally the **TENS:** $80 - 40$. That is 40.
The answer is 741.

Notice: Only the TENS digit will change (from 8 to 4)!
The "7" of the hundreds does not change, nor the "1" of the ones.

---

2. Subtract the whole tens. You can draw an illustration to help or use manipulatives.

a. $6\underline{5}0 - \underline{3}0 =$ _____	**b.** $570 - 60 =$ _____
c. $468 - 30 =$ _____	**d.** $294 - 80 =$ _____

3. Subtract. Compare the problems.

a.	**b.**	**c.**
$50 - 20 =$ _____	$70 - 30 =$ _____	$54 - 40 =$ _____
$150 - 20 =$ _____	$570 - 30 =$ _____	$154 - 40 =$ _____
$650 - 20 =$ _____	$870 - 30 =$ _____	$754 - 40 =$ _____

4. Subtract from the number shown in the illustration. Use the grid
   (subtract in columns).

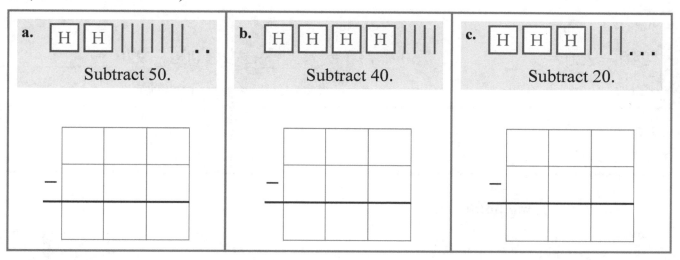

5. *Explain* in your own words *how* to subtract 683 – 50.

6. Grandpa Jerry lives alone. Each week, he pays $100 for rent and $80 for food.
   What is the total that Grandpa Jerry pays for those two things each week?

7. Greg picked 245 apples and Ryan picked 30 fewer apples than Greg.
   How many apples did Ryan pick?

8. Janet works after school on Tuesdays and Thursdays, and gets paid $25 each day.
   She also works on Saturdays and gets paid $50.

   How much does she earn in one week?

   In two weeks?

   In three weeks?

   How many weeks will she need to work to earn
   enough money to buy a bicycle for $350?

9. Solve each subtraction by thinking of the difference or of the "how many more" addition.

a.	b.	c.
240 − 220 = _____	760 − 710 = _____	1000 − 920 = _____
(220 + _____ = 240)	(difference of 760 and 710)	(920 + _____ = 1000)
d.	**e.**	**f.**
590 − 500 = _____	996 − 966 = _____	452 − 432 = _____

10. Fill in the missing numbers.

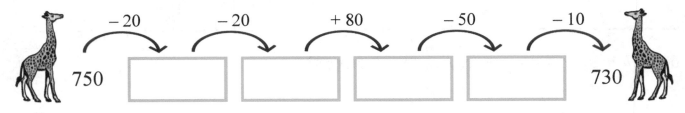

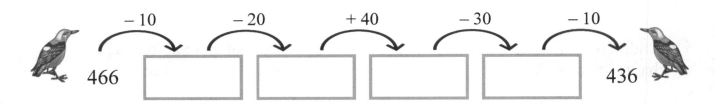

Puzzle Corner   **a.** Put the + or − signs into the squares in many different ways so that you get different answers.

500 ☐ 40 ☐ 50 = _____   200 ☐ 20 ☐ 70 = _____

500 ☐ 40 ☐ 50 = _____   200 ☐ 20 ☐ 70 = _____

500 ☐ 40 ☐ 50 = _____   200 ☐ 20 ☐ 70 = _____

500 ☐ 40 ☐ 50 = _____   200 ☐ 20 ☐ 70 = _____

b. Use the numbers 90, 70, and 40, and + or − signs, and make number sentences like those above.

What is the smallest possible answer?

What is the greatest possible answer?

Patterns and Problems

1. Three children played a card game where you get points for the cards left in your hand. The person who has the <u>least</u> points at the end of the game is the winner. The table shows the point count at a certain time in the game:

Then, Dan got 100 more points and Bill got 30 more points (Jim got none).

Add those to their point counts and write the new point counts in the grid.

The game ended now. Who won?

Jim	Dan	Bill
540	270	330

2. The bar graph shows how much money the Riley family spent for groceries in four different weeks.

   a. Mark above each bar how much they spent for groceries in dollars.

   b. How much more did they pay for week 3 than for week 4?

   c. How much more did they pay for week 2 than for week 1?

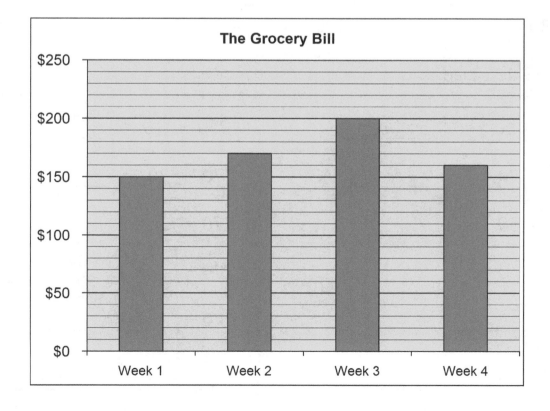

3. Count by 20s, and fill in the grid.

520	540	560		
620				
820				
				1000

4. Fill in.

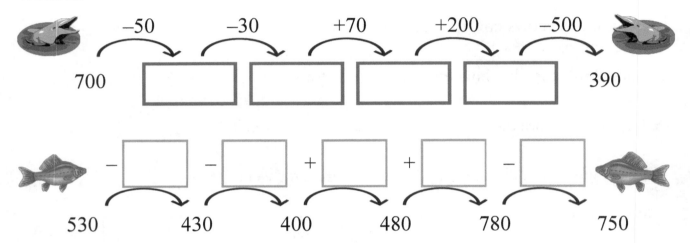

5. Continue the patterns!

a. 590 − 60 = _____	**b.** 770 + 10 = _____
590 − 70 = _____	770 + 20 = _____
590 − 80 = _____	770 + 30 = _____
590 − _____ = _____	770 + _____ = _____
590 − _____ = _____	770 + _____ = _____
590 − _____ = _____	770 + _____ = _____

44

6. Find what number goes in the oval.

Subtractions where the TOTAL is missing:	a. ( ) − 60 = 220	b. ( ) − 80 = 510
	c. ( ) − 500 = 100	d. ( ) − 310 = 60

e. 450 + ( ) = 750	f. 716 + ( ) = 776	"How many more" additions
g. 530 + ( ) = 590	h. 637 + ( ) = 697	

What was subtracted is missing:	i. 1000 − ( ) = 700	j. 740 − ( ) = 40
	k. 667 − ( ) = 607	l. 999 − ( ) = 299

Find what number goes into the oval!   Puzzle Corner

a. 980 − 200 − ( ) = 80	b. 784 − ( ) − 40 = 704
c. 210 + 50 + ( ) = 310	d. 600 + ( ) + 30 = 720

Bar Graphs and Pictographs

> *Bar graphs* use "bars" or rectangles in them to show some information.

1. This bar graph shows how many hours some second grade students slept last night.

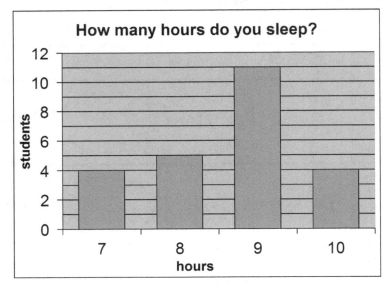

a. How many students slept 8 hours last night?

b. How many students slept 10 hours last night?

c. *How many more* students slept 9 hours than the ones who slept 10 hours?

d. A school nurse said that children need to sleep well for at least 8 hours. How many students slept *less than* 8 hours last night?

e. How many students slept *at least* 8 hours last night?

f. Make a pictograph. Draw ONE sleepy face to mean <u>2 students</u>.

	Students
Students who slept less than 8 hours	
Students who slept at least 8 hours	

2. Below, you see page counts for 14 different second grade math books.

217 388 365 290 304 315 243 352 289 392 346 308 329 323

Count how many books have between 200 and 249 pages.

Count how many books have between 250 and 299 pages.

Continue. Write the total pages in the chart.

Page count	Number of books
200-249	
250-299	
300-349	
350-399	

After that, draw a bar graph using the numbers in the above chart.

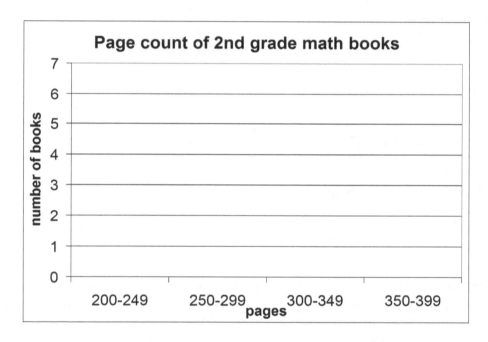

a. How many books had a page count between 350 and 399 pages?

b. How many books had 300 pages or more?

c. How many books had less than 250 pages?

d. What was the lowest page count?

3. The *pictograph* shows how many people visited the fairgrounds on different days. Each ☺ symbol means 100 people. Half a symbol (means 50 people. Draw a bar graph.

Day	
Thursday	☺☺☺(
Friday	☺☺☺☺☺
Saturday	☺☺☺☺☺☺☺☺(
Sunday	☺☺☺☺☺☺(

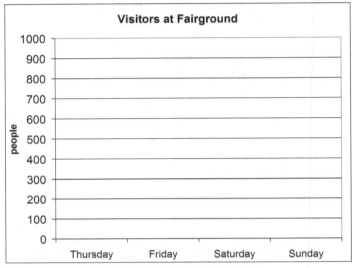

a. What was the most popular day of the fair?
How many people visited on that day?

b. How many more people visited on Sunday than on Friday?

c. What was the total number of visitors on Thursday and Friday?

d. Which day would you have gone, if you didn't like to be in a crowd?

Which day would you have gone, if you liked to be in a crowd?

4. Joe practiced basketball. Make a *pictograph* showing how many baskets he made each day. Draw a picture and decide how many baskets that picture represents.

Day	Baskets
Mon	80
Tue	60
Wed	100
Thu	30

Day	Baskets
Mon	
Tue	
Wed	
Thu	

5. The bars in a bar graph can be this way too, (sideways) like they are lying down.

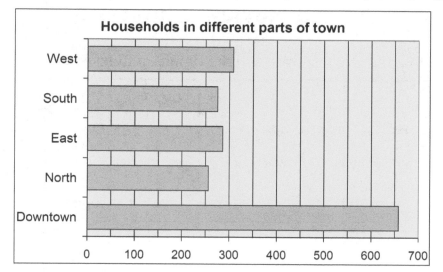

These numbers are in *scrambled* order, and they tell us *how many* households are in different parts of town: 275, 658, 256, 308, 286. Write the correct number after each bar on the graph.

6. (Optional) If you would like, make a *survey* among your class or friends. A survey means you ask many people the same question and write down what they answer. Then you make a graph. Some ideas:

- Ask many people what their favorite color is. Then make a bar graph.

- Ask many people what their eye color is. Then make a bar graph.

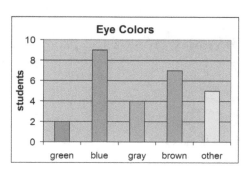

- Ask many people if they have a pet, and what pet it is. Then make a bar graph.

- Ask many people what their favorite game or sport is. Then make a bar graph.

Mixed Review Chapter 6

1. Write the time that the clock shows, and the time 5 minutes later.

	a.	b.	c.	d.
	___ : ___	___ : ___	___ : ___	___ : ___
5 min. later →	___ : ___	___ : ___	___ : ___	___ : ___

2. Find the missing numbers.

a. $16 - \square = 9$	b. $11 - \square = 3$	c. $12 - \square = 9$
d. $\square - 8 = 6$	e. $\square - 7 = 5$	f. $\square - 9 = 9$

3. Add. Compare the problems.

a. $7 + 6 =$ _____	b. $8 + 9 =$ _____	c. $5 + 8 =$ _____
$17 + 6 =$ _____	$68 + 9 =$ _____	$35 + 8 =$ _____

4. Mom divided 16 plums evenly between Jane and John. John ate 3 of his.
   Jane ate 2 of hers.
   How many does John have left?
   How many does Jane have left?

5. Write each number as a double of some other number.

a. $12 =$ ___ + ___	b. $18 =$ ___ + ___	c. $100 =$ ___ + ___
d. $40 =$ ___ + ___	e. $14 =$ ___ + ___	f. $600 =$ ___ + ___

6. Add.

a.	b.	c.	d.	e.
7 5	1 8	2 4	3 7	5 1
2 6	2 7	5 5	2 8	2 9
+2 4	+5 9	+2 5	3 7	9
			+2 3	+1 5

7. Draw a square in the grid that
   has 9 little squares inside.

8. Draw a rectangle in the grid that
   has 12 little squares inside.
   Can you draw another one with
   a different shape?

9. Divide the shapes into two, three, or four equal parts so that you can color
   the fraction.

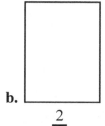

a.

$$\frac{1}{4}$$

b.

$$\frac{2}{3}$$

c.

$$\frac{3}{3}$$

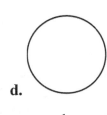

d.

$$\frac{1}{2}$$

10. Color. Then compare and write < , > , or = . Which is more "pie" to eat?

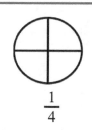

a.
$$\frac{3}{3} \qquad \frac{2}{2}$$

b.
$$\frac{1}{3} \qquad \frac{1}{4}$$

c.
$$\frac{2}{3} \qquad \frac{3}{4}$$

Review Chapter 6

1. **a.** Write the number shown by the image: _____

   b. Write the number that is 1 more
   than the number in the image: _____

   c. Write the number that is 10 more
   than the number in the image: _____

   d. Write the number that is 100 more
   than the number in the image: _____

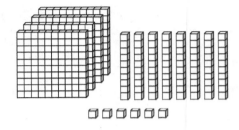

2. Write the numbers that come before and after the given number.

   a. _____ , 179 , _____   **b.** _____ , 201 , _____

   c. _____ , 800 , _____   **d.** _____ , 917 , _____

3. Write with numbers.

a. 700 + 9 = _____	**b.** 70 + 600 + 4 = _____
c. 80 + 500 = _____	**d.** 8 + 500 + 50 = _____

4. Count by fives: _____, _____, _____, _____, 715, 720.

5. Write the numbers that are 10 less and 10 more than the given number.

   a. _____, 292, _____   **b.** _____, 545, _____

6. Count by 20s, and fill in the grid.

200	220	240		
300				

7. Compare. Write < or > in the box.

a. 238 ☐ 265	b. 391 ☐ 193	c. 405 ☐ 450	d. 981 ☐ 819
e. 8 + 600 ☐ 60 + 800		f. 30 + 300 + 5 ☐ 90 + 8 + 100	

8. Arrange the three numbers in order, from the smallest to the biggest.

a. 109, 901, 199	b. 717, 175, 177

9. Add in columns.

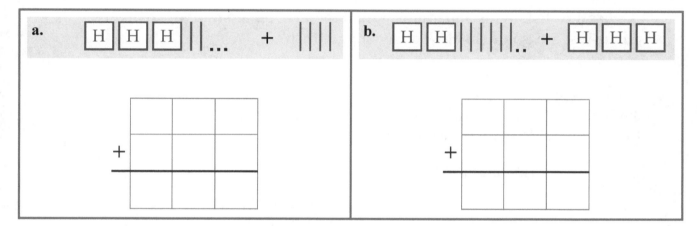

10. Add and subtract whole hundreds.

a.	b.	c.
720 + 200 = _____	508 + 400 = _____	219 + 500 = _____
780 − 300 = _____	670 − 400 = _____	954 − 900 = _____

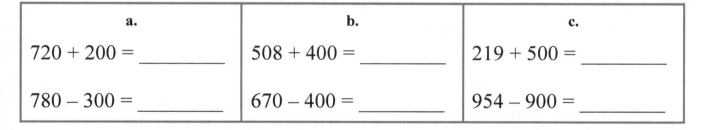

11. Add and subtract whole tens. You can underline the tens to help you.

a.	b.	c.
5<u>8</u>0 + <u>2</u>0 = _____	969 − 40 = _____	572 − 30 = _____
620 + 70 = _____	433 + 20 = _____	884 − 70 = _____

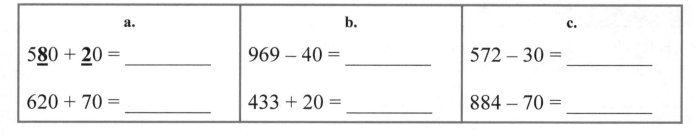

12. Fill in.

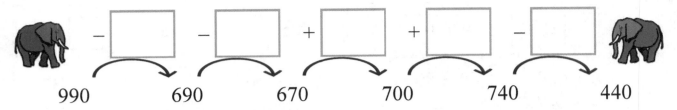

990   690   670   700   740   440

13. Solve the word problems.

a. Grandpa had 250 sheep. During 1 week, wolves killed 10 of them,
but 20 new little lambs were born.
How many sheep were in the flock at the end of the week?

b. Jake has 170 fish in his aquariums. Of all the fish, 30 are rainbow fish,
and the rest are goldfish. How many are goldfish?

c. Jake bought 50 more goldfish and 70 more rainbow fish.
How many goldfish does he have now?

And how many rainbow fish?

d. Sandra traveled 400 km in an airplane, and then 30 km in a car,
to go visit her mother. Then she returned the same way.
How many kilometers did Sandra travel?

Mystery Number

a. If you count by 10s from this number
3 times, you will get to 62.

b. It is less than 10. If you double it, you get a number
that is more than 10, but it will not be 14, 18, or 12.

Chapter 7: Measuring
Introduction

The seventh chapter of *Math Mammoth Grade 2* covers measuring length and weight. The child measures and estimates length in inches and half-inches, and learns to measure to the nearest half-inch or to the nearest centimeter. The bigger units—feet, miles, meters, and kilometers—are introduced, but in this grade level we do not yet study conversions between the units.

If you have the downloadable version of this book (PDF file), you need to print these lessons as 100%, not "shrink to fit," "print to fit," or similar. If you print "shrink to fit," some exercises about measuring in inches and centimeters will not come out right, but will be "shrunk" compared to reality.

The lessons on measuring weight include several activities to do using a bathroom scales. The goal is to let students become familiar with pounds and kilograms, and have an idea of how many pounds or kilograms some common things weigh.

When it comes to measuring, experience is the best teacher. So, encourage your child to use measuring devices (such as a measuring tape, ruler, and scales), and to "play" with them. In this way, the various measuring units start to become a normal part of his/her life, and will never be forgotten.

The concrete activities we do in second grade are laying an important foundation for familiarizing the children with measuring units. In third grade, the study of measuring turns toward conversions between the different units. In case you wonder about volume, we will study that in third grade and onward.

The Lessons

Helpful Resources on the Internet

Use these free online resources to supplement the "bookwork" as you see fit.

Scan me

You can also access this list of links at https://links.mathmammoth.com/gr2ch7

Measure It!
Click on the ruler to measure a red bar.
https://www.funbrain.com/games/measure-it

Reading a tape measure worksheets
Worksheet generator: You can choose to what accuracy to measure, inches, or inches and feet.
https://themathworksheetsite.com/read_tape.html

Measuring Length in Inches
Identify the length of each object in this interactive online quiz.
https://www.softschools.com/measurement/games/ruler/measuring_length_in_inches/

Measuring in Centimeters
Practice measuring various objects using a metric ruler.
https://www.topmarks.co.uk/maths-games/measuring-in-cm

Measurement Quiz
Practice measuring fish in whole and half centimeters.
https://www.thatquiz.org/tq-9/?-j1-l2-mpnv600-p0

Measurement Workshop - Online
Build cities out of customary or metric rulers, or choose "play mode" to allow the program to randomly form a city, and then determine each ruler's height in inches or centimeters. Choose "Whole numbers".
https://mrnussbaum.com/measurement-workshop-online

Broken Centimeter Ruler
Use the metric ruler to measure the length of each of the lines. The ruler is broken, so be careful!
https://www.geogebra.org/m/D8rTXSAp

US Standard Measurements for Length
This page has clear explanations and good illustrations of the standard units for measuring length.
https://www.mathsisfun.com/measure/us-standard-length.html

Reading Scales: Mass
An interactive resource for illustrating different kinds of scales and how to read the measurements on the scales.
https://www.teacherled.com/iresources/scales/mass/

Measuring scales
An interactive scales for the purpose of demonstrating how a scales works. You can add weights to the scales and choose to show or hide the total weight.
https://mathsframe.co.uk/en/resources/resource/87/itp-measuring-scales

Mostly Postie!
Choose "kg and half kg". Place a package on the scale, and enter the reading, including the possible "1/2 kg."
https://www.ictgames.com/mobilePage/mostlyPostie/index.html

Measuring to the Nearest Centimeter

Remember? We can measure how long things are using *centimeters*.

This line is 1 centimeter long: ⊢—⊣
A centimeter is written in short form as "cm."
The blue line on the right is 6 cm long. →

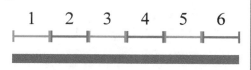

1. How many centimeters long are these lines?

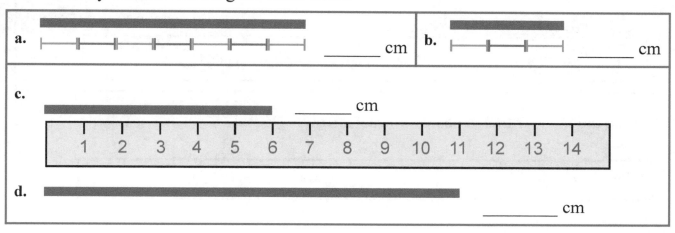

a. _____ cm

b. _____ cm

c. _____ cm

d. _____ cm

2. Measure the pencils with a centimeter ruler. If you don't have one, you can cut out the one from the bottom of this page. Then answer the questions.

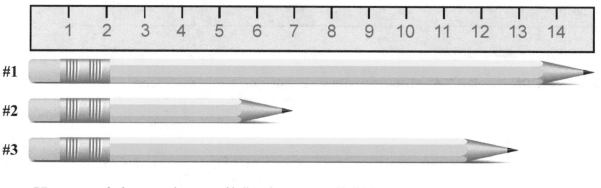

a. How much longer is pencil #1 than pencil #2? _____ cm

b. How much longer is pencil #3 than pencil #2? _____ cm

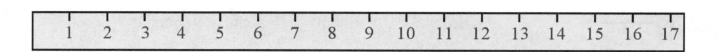

Most things are NOT exactly a certain number of whole centimeters.
You can measure them to the nearest centimeter.

The pencil below is a little over 10 cm long. It is *about 10* cm long.

This pencil is about 9 cm long. The end of the pencil is closer to 9 cm than to 8 cm.

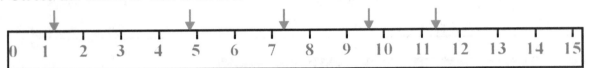

3. Circle the number that is nearest to each arrow.

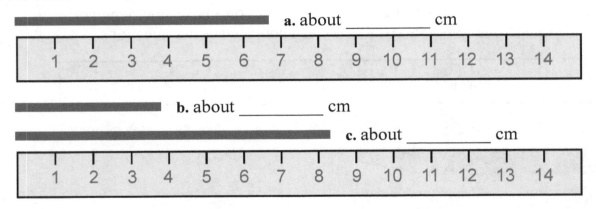

4. Measure the lines to the nearest centimeter.

      a. about _____ cm

      b. about _____ cm

      c. about _____ cm

5. This line is 1 cm long: ⊢—⊣ . Your finger is probably about that wide; put it
on top of the 1-cm line and check! Guess how long these lines are. Then measure.

	My guess:	**Measurement:**
a. ————————	about _____ cm	about _____ cm
b. ———	about _____ cm	about _____ cm
c. —————	about _____ cm	about _____ cm

6. **a.** Find two small objects. Measure to find *about* how many centimeters longer one is than the other.

The _____ is *about* _____ cm longer

than the _____.

b. Find other two small objects. Measure to find *about* how many centimeters longer one is than the other.

The _____ is *about* _____ cm longer

than the _____.

7. Draw some lines here or on blank paper. Use a <u>ruler</u>. Hold the ruler down tight with one hand, while drawing the line with the other. It takes some practice!

a. 6 cm long

b. 3 cm long

c. 12 cm long

8. Find some small objects. First GUESS how long or tall they are. Then measure. If the item is not exactly so-many centimeters long, then measure it to the nearest centimeter and write "about" before the centimeter-amount, such as *about 8 cm*.

Item	GUESS	MEASUREMENT
	cm	cm
	cm	cm
	cm	cm
	cm	cm
	cm	cm

Inches and Half-Inches

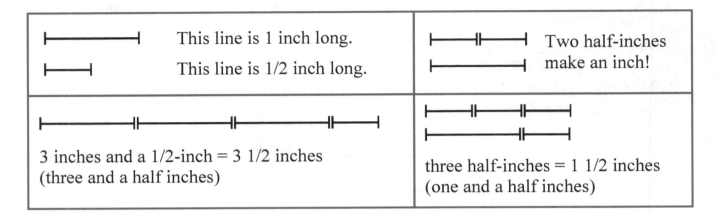

⊢—————⊣ This line is 1 inch long. ⊢——⊣ This line is 1/2 inch long.	⊢——⊩—⊣ Two half-inches ⊢————⊣ make an inch!
⊢——————⊩———⊩———⊩—⊣ 3 inches and a 1/2-inch = 3 1/2 inches (three and a half inches)	⊢——⊩——⊩—⊣ ⊢——————⊩—⊣ three half-inches = 1 1/2 inches (one and a half inches)

1. How long are the lines of inches and half-inches when placed end-to-end?

a. ⊢————⊩——⊣ _____ inches

b. ⊢————⊩—⊣ _____ inches

c. ⊢—⊩——⊩——⊩——⊩—⊣ _____ inches

d. ⊢————⊩————⊩————⊩————⊩—⊣ _____ in.

2. How long are these things in inches?

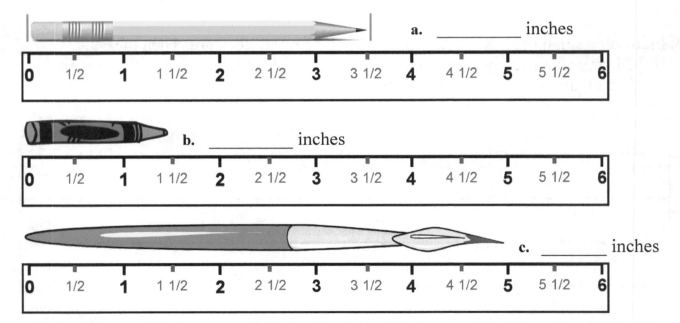

a. _____ inches

b. _____ inches

c. _____ inches

You can cut out one of the rulers in this lesson and tape it on an existing ruler or cardboard after you have finished the exercises on this and the next page!

Most objects are NOT exactly a certain number of whole inches, or even whole and half inches. You can measure them to the nearest inch, or to the nearest half-inch.

The pencil below is a little over 4 inches long. It is _about_ 4 inches long.

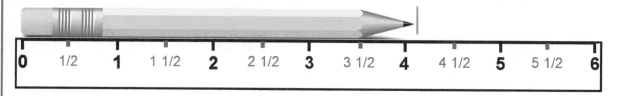

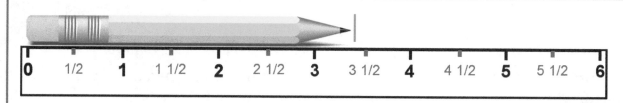

The pencil above is about 3 1/2 inches long. The end of the pencil is closer to 3 1/2 than to 3.

3. Circle the whole-inch or half-inch number that is nearest to each arrow.

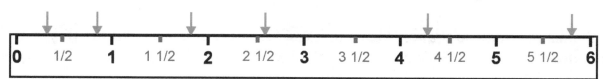

4. Measure the pencils to the nearest half-inch.

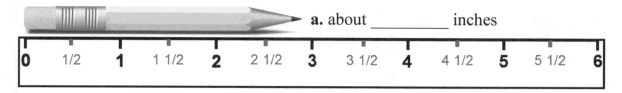

a. about _____ inches

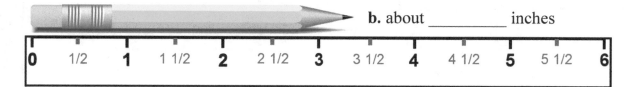

b. about _____ inches

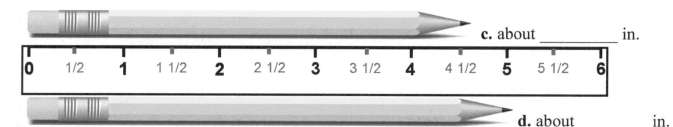

c. about _____ in.

d. about _____ in.

5. First GUESS how long these lines are in inches and half-inches. Write down your guess. After that, measure how long the lines are.

	GUESS	MEASUREMENT
a.	_____ inches	_____ inches
b.	_____ inches	_____ inches
c.	_____ inches	_____ inches

6. Draw some lines on a blank paper. Use a <u>ruler</u>. Hold the ruler down tight with one hand, while drawing the line with the other. It takes some practice!

   a. 5 in. long   **b.** 2 in. long

   c. 12 in. long **d.** 9 in. long

7. Write the names of these shapes. Measure the sides of the shapes. "All the way around" means you need to find the *total* length of the four sides (use addition!).

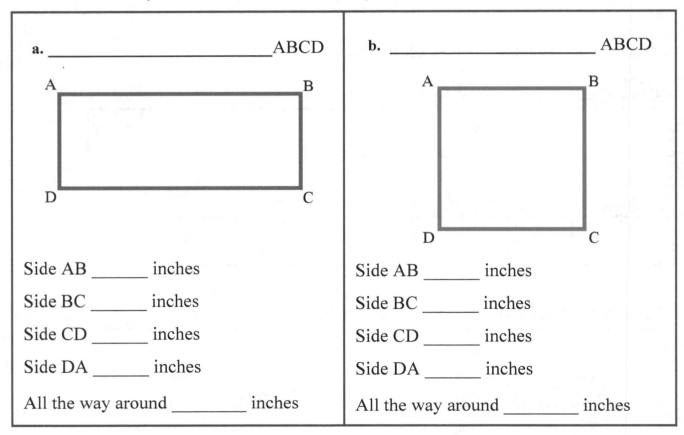

a. _____ABCD

A   B

D   C

Side AB _____ inches

Side BC _____ inches

Side CD _____ inches

Side DA _____ inches

All the way around _____ inches

b. _____ ABCD

A   B

D   C

Side AB _____ inches

Side BC _____ inches

Side CD _____ inches

Side DA _____ inches

All the way around _____ inches

Some More Measuring

1. Jackie measured the length of a bunch of pencils at her home. She recorded her results in a line plot below. For each pencil, she put an "x" mark above the number line, to show how many centimeters long it was.

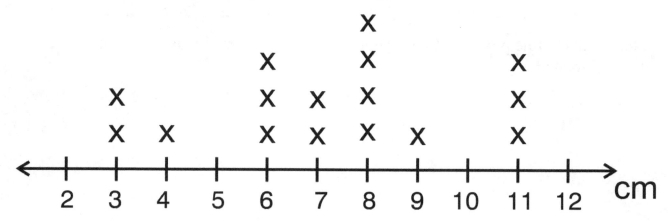

   a. How many of Jackie's pencils were 3 cm long?

   b. How many were 8 cm long?

   c. How many pencils were 9 cm *or* longer?

   d. How many pencils were 5 cm or shorter?

   e. Find how long Jackie's longest pencil is and her shortest pencil is.

   How much longer is the longest pencil than the shortest pencil?

2. Join these dots with lines to form a four-sided shape. What is the name for a four-sided shape? _____

   Measure its sides to the nearest centimeter. Write "about ___ cm" next to each side.

   How many centimeters is the *perimeter?* (all the way around the shape)

   It is _____ cm.

3. Measure many pencils of different lengths to the *nearest* whole centimeter.
Write the lengths below. (You don't have to measure as many pencils as there are empty lines.)

_____ cm, _____ cm, _____ cm, _____ cm, _____ cm, _____ cm

_____ cm, _____ cm, _____ cm, _____ cm, _____ cm, _____ cm

_____ cm, _____ cm, _____ cm, _____ cm, _____ cm, _____ cm

Now, make a line plot about your pencils like what Jackie made. Write an "X" mark
for each pencil.

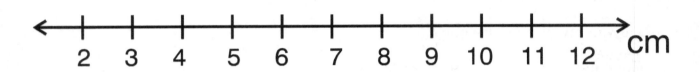

a. How much longer is your longest pencil than your shortest pencil?

b. If you take your three longest pencils and put them end-to-end,
how long is your line of pencils? Add to find out.

It is _____ cm.   (If you can, measure to check your answer.)

4. Measure all the sides of this triangle to the nearest half-inch.
Also, find the *perimeter* (all the way around the triangle).

Side AB _____ in.

Side BC _____ in.

Side CA _____ in.

Perimeter _____ in.

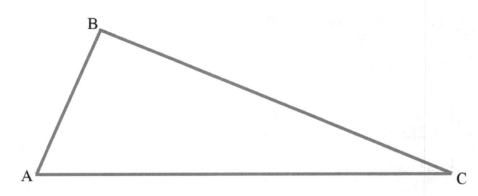

5. Measure some things in your classroom or at home *two times*. First measure them in inches, to the nearest half-inch. Them measure them in centimeters, to the nearest whole centimeter. Remember to write "about" if the thing is not exactly so many inches or centimeters. Write your results in the table below.

Item	in inches	in centimeters
	in.	cm
	in.	cm
	in.	cm
	in.	cm
	in.	cm

a. Which numbers are bigger, the centimeter-amounts or the inch-amounts?

b. Which measuring unit is bigger, one centimeter or one inch?

Notice: If your measuring unit is small (like 1 cm), you need MORE of them THAN if you use a longer measuring unit (inch).

c. Megan measured a spoon. It was 13 cm long. If she measures it in inches, will the result be more than 13 inches, or less than 13 in.?

d. Harry measured a toy car in inches. It was 3 in. If he measures it in centimeters, will the result be more than 3 cm, or less than 3 cm?

6. Draw three dots on a blank paper so you can join them and make a triangle. Then, measure its sides BOTH in inches (to the nearest half-inch) and in centimeters (to the nearest centimeter). Write your results in the table.

My Triangle	in inches	in centimeters
Side 1	in.	cm
Side 2	in.	cm
Side 3	in.	cm

How many centimeters is the *perimeter* (all the way around the shape)? _____ cm

How many inches is the *perimeter* (all the way around the shape)? _____ in.

Feet and Miles

This is a tape measure. The numbers 1, 2, 3, and so on, are inches.

Above number 12 you see "1F". That means *1 foot*. 12 inches equals 1 foot.

Unroll the tape measure some more, until you find "2 F" or "2 ft" (which means two feet), and "3 ft" (three feet), and so on. Stretch out the tape measure as far as you can. What is the most number of feet it has?

This tape measure has both inches and centimeters. The numbers on the top part are inches, and the numbers on the bottom part are centimeters. The number 60 means 60 cm, and the "1" after it means 61 cm.

You use *feet* as your measuring unit when you measure the width of a room or of a table, the length of a house, or of a swimming pool.

People often use both feet and inches. For example, a table can be 5 feet 10 inches long. Or, a boy can be 4 ft. 7 in. tall. How tall are you in feet and inches?

1. Use a tape measure to find distances in feet, or feet and inches. Let an adult help you.

Thing or distance	How long / tall
the room you are in	
a table	

2. How tall are these people? Ask your mom, dad, or others.

You: _____ ft _____ in   _____ : _____ ft _____ in

Your mom: _____ ft _____ in   _____ : _____ ft _____ in

3. Find three things you can measure in feet. But wait! First *guess* how long or tall
   they are. Then, check your guess by measuring.

Thing or distance	My guess	How long / tall

4. Now, measure again some of the things you already measured in feet, but this time
   measure them in centimeters. Or, you can still find new things to measure.

Thing or distance	centimeters	feet & inches

5. Which is a bigger (or longer) measuring unit, 1 centimeter or 1 foot?

   Jared measured the height of a fridge twice, first in feet and then in centimeters.

   It was 5 ft tall. How tall was it in centimeters?   **a.** 15 cm   **b.** 150 cm   **c.** 3 cm

6. He also measured the height of a bucket twice, in feet and then in centimeters.

   It was 60 cm tall. How tall was it in feet?   **a.** 6 ft   **b.** 100 ft   **c.** 2 ft

7. Which is a longer measuring unit, a meter or a foot?

   Jared measured the length of his room twice, first using feet and then using meters.

   It was 4 m wide. How many feet wide was it?   **a.** 2 ft   **b.**5 ft   **c.** 12 ft

> Distances between towns or between countries are measured in _miles_.
> 1 mile is 5,280 feet (five-thousand two-hundred eighty)! That is a lot of
> feet—many, many more than your tape measure has.

8. Can you think of familiar distances in everyday life or in your neighborhood that are so many miles? An adult can help. You can also look in your social studies book.

Distance	How many miles

9. Aaron went on a trip with his family. On the first day, they drove 80 miles and visited a nature park. On the second day, they drove 200 miles. On the third day, they drove 110 miles back home.

   a. How long a distance did the family drive in all?

   b. How much longer distance did they drive on the second day than on the first day?

10. Which unit would you use to find the following distances: inches (in), feet (ft), miles (mi), or feet and inches (ft. in.)?

Distance	Unit
from New York to Los Angeles	
from a house to a neighbor's	
the width of a notebook	
the distance around the earth	
how tall a refrigerator is	
the width of a porch	
the length of a board	

Distance	Unit
the length of a train	
the length of a playground	
from a train station to the next	
the width of a computer screen	

Meters and Kilometers

We use _meters_ to measure medium and long distances.

Find a tape measure that has centimeters.
Find the 100th centimeter on it. That is the 1-meter point.

<u>100 centimeters equals 1 meter.</u>

1. **a.** Mark **one meter** on the floor. Can you take such a big step?
Can the teacher?

   b. On the 1-metre line you marked, practice taking <u>two</u> steps that together are 1 meter long. Take similar steps to _estimate_ the length of a room (or building if outside).
Count your steps: I took _____ steps
Since you took 2 steps for each meter, find half of your count to get the length in meters. The room is about _____ m long.

   Measure to check your estimation.

   You can repeat this to estimate some other distance or length.

2. How tall are these people? Measure, or ask your mom, dad and friends.

You: _____ cm   _____ : _____ cm

Your mom: _____ cm   _____ : _____ cm

Your dad: _____ cm   _____ : _____ cm

3. Measure some things using meters and centimeters. First guess how long or tall they are. Then check your guesses by measuring. Let an adult help you.

Item	My guess	How long/tall

> Distances between towns or between countries are measured in _kilometers_.
> 1 kilometer is 1 000 meters (one thousand meters)!

4. Write in the table below **three distances** that are important in your life and are measured in kilometers. Ask an adult to help you. Examples include: from home to the library, from home to downtown, from home to Grandmother's, from your town to the capital city, etc.

From ... to	distance in km

5. The picture shows the field for Finnish baseball game ("pesäpallo"). How many meters do you run with these "routes"?

a. You run from the home base to the 1st base and then return to the home base.

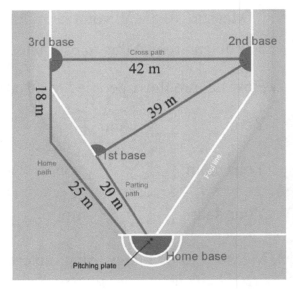

b. You run from the home base to the 1st base and on to the 2nd base, plus one meter over, because you cannot stop in time.

c. (Challenge) You run all the way around the field.

6. Which unit would you use to find these below: centimeters (cm), meters (m), or kilometers (km)?

Distance	Unit	Distance	Unit
the length of a park		around your wrist	
from Tshwane to the North Pole		the height of a room	
the length of a cell phone		the length of an airplane trip	
the length of a bus		the length of a grasshopper	

Weight in Pounds

Weight means *how heavy* something is. You can measure weight using a scale.
A bathroom scale measures weight in *pounds* or in *kilograms*.

In this lesson you will need:

- a bathroom scale that measures in pounds
- a bucket and water
- encyclopedias or some other fairly heavy books
- a plastic bag or some other bag
- a backpack

The numbers on your scale may go up by twenties, and not by tens. In the picture here, the longer line halfway in-between the two numbers is <u>TEN more</u> than the smaller of the two numbers. Each little line means 2 pounds more than the previous line.

The scale on the right is stopped at the second little line after 140 pounds, which means 140 + 2 + 2 pounds, or 144 pounds.

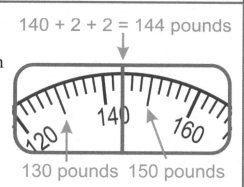

We use "lb" to abbreviate the word pounds. 15 pounds = 15 lb.
The "lb" comes from the Latin word *libra*, which also means a pound.

1. How many pounds is the scale showing? You can mark the in-between ten-numbers on the scale to help.

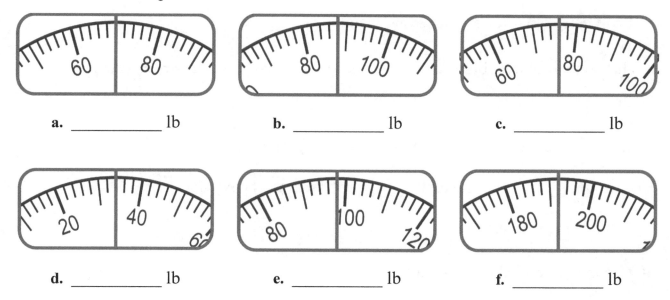

a. _____ lb

b. _____ lb

c. _____ lb

d. _____ lb

e. _____ lb

f. _____ lb

2. Step onto the scale. I weigh _____ pounds.

3. Find out how many pounds your family members weigh. Write a list below.

_____ _____ lb _____ _____ lb

_____ _____ lb _____ _____ lb

_____ _____ lb _____ _____ lb

4. Weigh some other items. Note that on a bathroom scale, you cannot weigh very
   light items, nor very big and bulky ones because you can't place them on the scales.

a bucket full of water   _____ lb   Mom's skillet   _____ lb

a bucket half full of water   _____ lb   _____ _____ lb

a stack of heavy books   _____ lb   _____ _____ lb

5. Find out how many pounds of water you can carry. Can you carry the bucket when it
   is full? If not, pour out some water until you can carry the bucket.

   I can carry a bucket of water that weighs _____ lb.

6. **a.** Find out how many pounds of books you can carry in a bag. Fill the bag with
   books and weigh it. Can you carry it? If not, take out some books until you
   are able to carry the bag.

   I can carry a bagful of books that weighs _____ lb.

   b. The same as above, but use a backpack. (Do you think you can carry more or less?)

   I can carry a backpack that weighs _____ lb.

   c. Weigh yourself with and without a heavy bag of books.

   I weigh _____ lb. I weigh _____ lb with the heavy bag.

   What is the difference? _____ lb.

   d. Use the method above with a heavy book. The book weighs _____ lb.

Weight in Kilograms

Weight means _how heavy_ something is. You can measure weight using _a scale_. A bathroom scale measures weight in _kilograms_ (abbreviated kg).

The scale usually has short lines for each kilogram increment, and long lines for each 10 kilograms. In the picture below, the in-between numbers ending in "5" are marked with the number 5.

In this lesson, you need to use a bathroom scale that measures weight in kilograms. You will also need

- a bucket and water
- encyclopedias or some other fairly heavy books
- a plastic bag or some other bag
- a backpack

The scale is showing 22 kg.

1. How many kilograms is the scale showing?

a. _____   b. _____   c. _____

2. Step onto the scale. How much do you weigh? _____ kg

3. Find out how many kilograms your family members weigh. Write a list below.

_____ _____ kg _____ _____ kg

_____ _____ kg _____ _____ kg

_____ _____ kg _____ _____ kg

4. Also, weigh some of your family members together.

_____ and _____ together weigh _____ kg.

_____ and _____ together weigh _____ kg.

5. Now weigh some other items with the bathroom scale. Note: you cannot weigh very light items on it. You also cannot weigh very big and bulky items (such as tables) on it because you can't place them fully on the scale. Try to find objects that are not very big.

a bucket full of water _____ kg   Mom's frying pan _____ kg

a bucket half full of water _____ kg   _____ _____ kg

a stack of heavy books _____ kg   _____ _____ kg

6. Find out how many kilograms of water you can carry. Can you carry the bucket when it is full? If not, pour out some water until you can carry the bucket.

I can carry a bucket of water that weighs _____ kg.

7. **a.** Find out how many kilograms of books you can carry in a bag. Fill the bag with books and weigh it. Can you carry it? If not, take out some books until you are able to carry the bag.

I can carry a bagful of books that weighs _____ kg.

b. The same as above, but use a backpack.

I can carry a backpack that weighs _____ kg.

c. Weigh yourself with and without the heavy bag of books.

I weigh _____ kg. I weigh _____ kg with the heavy bag.

What is the difference? _____ kg.

You can use this method to weigh items that cannot easily be placed on the scales, but that you can hold.

d. Weigh yourself with and without a heavy book.

I weigh _____ kg. I weigh _____ kg with the heavy book.

What is the difference? _____ kg. So, the book weighs _____ kg.

Mixed Review Chapter 7

1. Fill in.

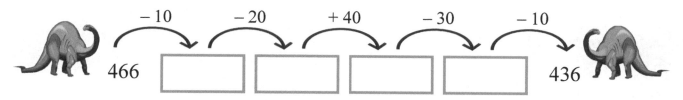

2. One of the "parts" for the numbers is missing. Solve what number the triangle is.

a. 700 + △ + 5 = 735	b. 400 + 40 + △ = 449	c. 7 + △ + 90 = 297
△ = _____	△ = _____	△ = _____

3. Skip-count by tens.

a. 806, 816, _____, _____, _____, _____, _____, _____

b. 542, 532, _____, _____, _____, _____, _____, _____

4. Skip-count by fives.

a. 280, 285, _____, _____, _____, _____, _____, _____

b. 1000, 995, _____, _____, _____, _____, _____, _____

5. Find the double of these numbers.

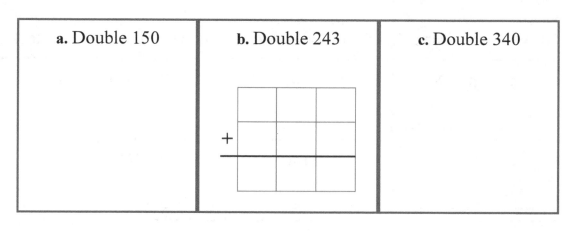

6. Draw some lines on a blank paper. Use a <u>ruler</u>. Hold the ruler down tight with one hand, while drawing the line with the other. It takes some practice!

    a. 3 in. long

    b. 8 in. long

    c. 12 cm long

    d. 7 cm long

7. Aaron visited an amusement park with his family that was 90 km away. They drove there and back. How many kilometers did the family drive all totaled?

8. Which unit would you use to find these below: centimeters (cm), meters (m), or kilometers (km)?

Distance	Unit
from Pretoria to Durban	
the length of your room	
the length of a pencil	

Distance	Unit
around your neck	
the width of a butterfly	
how far you can throw a ball	

9. The total is missing from each subtraction sentence. Solve.

    a. $\boxed{} - 5 = 24$ **b.** $\boxed{} - 60 = 420$ **c.** $\boxed{} - 500 = 240$

10. Write the time using the **hours:minutes** way. Use your practice clock to help.

a. 10 past 8	b. 15 till 7	c. 25 past 12	d. half-past 7
_____ : _____	_____ : _____	_____ : _____	_____ : _____
e. 9 o'clock	f. 20 till 6	g. 5 till 11	h. 25 till 4
_____ : _____	_____ : _____	_____ : _____	_____ : _____

11. Write the dates in the form (*month*) (*day*) (*year*), such as June 15, 2011.

	month	day	year
a. today's date	_____	_____	_____
b. tomorrow's date	_____	_____	_____
c. your birthday this year	_____	_____	_____
d. your friend's birthday this year	_____	_____	_____

12. **a.** Draw here a big and a small three-sided shape. What are three-sided shapes called?

   b. Draw here a red six-sided shape and a blue four-sided shape. What are six-sided shapes called?

The DIGITS of the number 467 are 4, 6, and 7. The sum of its digits is 4 + 6 + 7 = 17 (just add its digits).

Find a number that...

- is more than 100 but less than 200;
- the sum of its digits is 11.

There are actually 9 different numbers like that. Can you find all of them?

Puzzle Corner

Review Chapter 7

1. Which unit or units would you use for the following distances: inches (in.), feet (ft), miles (mi), centimeters (cm), or meters (m)? If two different units work, write both.

Distance	Unit or units
from your house to the grocery store	
from Miami to New York	
the distance across the room	
the height of a bookcase	

2. Measure this line to the nearest centimeter and to the nearest half-inch.

about _____ cm _or_ about _____ in.

3. **a.** Draw a line that is 3 1/2 inches long.

b. Draw a line that is 9 cm long.

4. Measure these two pencils to the nearest centimeter, _and_ to the nearest half-inch. Then fill in:

The longer pencil is about _____ cm longer than the shorter one.

The longer pencil is about _____ inches longer than the shorter one.

5. Measure the width and length of the room you are in. First, measure them using feet and inches. Then, measure them using meters and centimeters.

Width: _____ ft _____ in _or_ _____ m _____ cm

Length: _____ ft _____ in _or_ _____ m _____ cm

Chapter 8: Regrouping in Addition and Subtraction
Introduction

The eighth chapter of *Math Mammoth Grade 2* deals with regrouping in addition (a.k.a. carrying) and in subtraction (a.k.a. borrowing). Regrouping in subtraction in particular can be somewhat challenging to some children. The free videos matched to the curriculum at **https://www.mathmammoth.com/videos/** (choose 2nd grade videos) can be used to help teach these topics.

In the first lesson, the child adds three-digit numbers with a regrouping in tens, but there is no regrouping in hundreds. Children already know how to regroup two-digit numbers, so this lesson simply extends that knowledge to numbers with three digits.

In the next lesson, children regroup 10 tens as a hundred (or carry to the hundreds). This is first illustrated with a visual model. You can adapt those exercises to be done with manipulatives instead, if desired.

Then we study regrouping twice: 10 ones form a new ten, and then 10 tens form a new hundred. Again, children first work with visual models, with the aim of helping them to understand the concept itself. Then, they learn the abstract process, adding the numbers in columns (one number written under the other).

Next, we study regrouping in subtraction, starting with two-digit numbers. First, children are taught to break one ten into 10 ones. For example, 5 tens 4 ones is written as 4 tens 14 ones; one of the tens is "broken down" into 10 ones. This is the process of regrouping: one of the tens "changes groups" from being with the tens to being with the ones.

After mastering that process, it is time to use regrouping in subtraction problems and learn the traditional paper-and-pencil method of subtracting (where one number is written under the other).

Then we study word problems that include the thought of "more" or "fewer", and also several techniques or "tricks" for mental subtraction. Please note that the word problems in this chapter require both addition and subtraction. I do not include only subtraction word problems in a lesson that is about subtraction, because children need to learn to recognize whether a problem requires addition or subtraction. Thus, the word problem sets always include both addition and subtraction word problems.

After this, it is time to study regrouping in subtraction with three-digit numbers. There are four cases:

1. Regrouping one ten as 10 ones, such as is necessary in $546 - 229$.
2. Regrouping one hundred as 10 tens, such as is necessary in $728 - 441$.
3. Regrouping two times (one ten as 10 ones, and one hundred as 10 tens), such as in $725 - 448$.
4. Regrouping with zero tens, such as is necessary in $405 - 278$.

In second grade, we only study cases (1) and (2) from the list above. The other two cases are left for third grade.

In the end of the chapter, children encounter bar graphs again. They also play Euclid's game, which is meant as a fun, supplemental lesson. You may omit it if time does not allow.

The Lessons

Helpful Resources on the Internet

Use these free online resources to supplement the "bookwork" as you see fit.

You can also access this list of links at **https://links.mathmammoth.com/gr2ch8**

Scan me

Two-Digit Addition & Subtraction with Mental Math — Online Practice
Choose between the various subtraction options to practice mental subtraction, as taught in this chapter. This program also works as offline in most browsers.
https://www.mathmammoth.com/practice/addition-subtraction-two-digit.php

Number Pieces
Virtual base-ten blocks that you can use to model regrouping.
https://www.mathlearningcenter.org/resources/apps/number-pieces

Addition Quiz
Practice 3-digit addition in columns in this online quiz.
https://www.thatquiz.org/tq-1/?-jg41-lk-p0

Tic-Tac-Toe Addition
Practice adding on a Tic-Tac-Toe grid. Choose "Addition/Hard".
https://www.funbrain.com/games/tic-tac-toe-squares

Vertical Addition Colors Game — 3-Digit Addition with Regrouping
Practice your addition skills in this interactive exercise.
https://www.mathmammoth.com/practice/vertical-addition#max=999&questions=3*3&addends=2

Puzzle Pics Addition
Solve the addition problems to reveal the mystery picture.
https://www.mathplayground.com/puzzle_pics_addition.html

Stop Before 1000

Use addition to come as close as you can to 1000 without going over. Note: Loads very slowly in Chrome, and doesn't work in Firefox.

https://www.learnalberta.ca/content/me3us/flash/lessonLauncher.html?lesson=lessons/06/m3_06_00_x.swf

Partial Pyramids

Complete the pyramids so that the numbers in each brick is the sum of the two numbers in the bricks below.

https://www.transum.org/Maths/Exercise/Pyramid/

SUBTRACTION

Hidden Picture Subtraction Game

Uncover a hidden picture by clicking on the correct answers to the subtraction problems.

https://www.mathmammoth.com/practice/mystery-picture-subtraction#min=3&max=50

Base Ten Blocks

Illustrate regrouping with base ten blocks. First form a number, such as 41, that you subtract from. Then show the child how one of the tens is broken down into ten ones, before subtracting.

https://www.coolmath4kids.com/manipulatives/base-ten-blocks

Vertical Subtraction Colors Game — 2-Digit Subtraction with Regrouping

Practice vertical (column) subtraction with regrouping, with this fun and colorful online game!

https://www.mathmammoth.com/practice/vertical-subtraction#max=99&zeros=0&questions=4*3

Subtraction Action

Click on numbers in the grid that add up to the missing number in the subtraction problem.

https://games.forkids.education/subtraction-action/

10-Question Subtraction Quiz

Practice basic subtraction concepts in this online quiz.

https://www.thatquiz.org/tq-1/?-jg42-l5-p0

Puzzle Pics Subtraction

Solve the subtraction problems to reveal the mystery picture.

https://www.mathplayground.com/puzzle_pics_subtraction.html

Subtraction by Splitting

Practice subtraction by splitting numbers. Choose the "Advanced" level.

https://games.forkids.education/the-amoeba-subtraction-game/

Triple-Digit Subtraction Card Game

Practice making the smallest difference. This card game requires two players.

http://www.mathgamesandactivities.com/tag/math-games-that-involve-regrouping/

GRAPHS AND PROBLEMS

Addition and Subtraction Word Problems

Interactive online word problems that practice addition and subtraction.

https://www.mathplayground.com/wpdatabase/05a.html

Word Problems

Practice addition and subtraction with this set of five word problems.

https://www.mathplayground.com/wpdatabase/Addition_Subtraction_2DigitNRG_10.htm

Thatquiz.org Quiz for Graphs

A 10-question quiz involving bar graphs and pictographs.

https://www.thatquiz.org/tq-5/?-j40v0h-l1-p0

Adding 3-Digit Numbers in Columns

When the numbers have three digits, adding them in columns (where you write the numbers under each other) is still easy. We just add hundreds in their own column.

	hundreds	tens	ones
	2	4	1
+	3	3	5
	5	7	6

Regrouping in the tens happens the same way as what you have learned before.

Ten ones form a new ten. This new ten is regrouped with the other tens. We write a little "1" above the other tens in the tens' column.

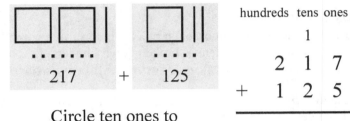

217   +   125

Circle ten ones to make a new ten!

	hundreds	tens	ones
		1	
	2	1	7
+	1	2	5
	3	4	2

1. Write the numbers to be added in the grid, and add. Regroup.

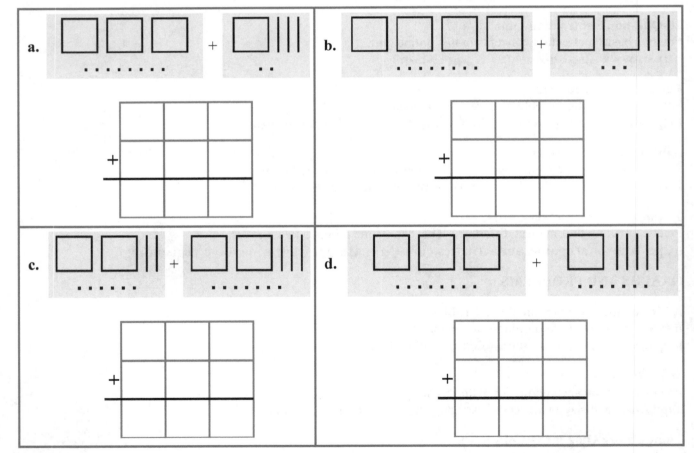

2. Add. Regroup 10 ones as a ten if necessary. Add hundreds in their own column.

a. 3 0 1 + 5 1 0	**b.** 2 2 7 + 5 3 6	**c.** 4 0 2 + 3 7 0	**d.** 1 2 9 + 4 5 4

e.   2 0 7
      2 2 3
 + 4 3 6
	f. 4 3 7
	      1 1 5
	 + 4 3 7
		g. 2 2 4
		      3 0 1
		 + 4 0 8
			h. 2 3 2
			      3 0 8
			 + 4 2 5

3. **a.** A factory had 547 workers. Then the factory hired 128 more workers. How many workers are there now?

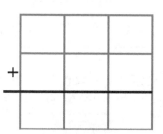

b. One bag contains 100 balloons. You bought six bags of balloons. Then you blew up 20 balloons. How many balloons are left in the bags?

c. Nancy bought three bookcases. Each bookcase cost $116. What was the total cost?

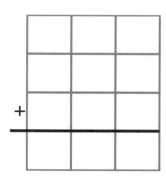

What numbers are missing from the additions?

Puzzle Corner

```
  □ 3 □        2 □ □        1 1 6        □ 4 7
+ 1 □ 5      + □ 5 5      + □ 5 □      + 7 □ □
-------      -------      -------      -------
  7 7 6        5 8 0        5 □ 3        9 9 2
```

Regrouping 10 Tens As a Hundred

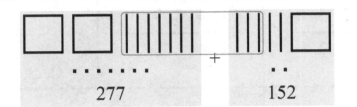

hundreds	tens	ones
1		
2	7	7
+ 1	5	2
4	2	9

277   152

Ten TENS are grouped to make a new hundred!

In the TENS, there are 7 tens and 5 tens to add (277 has 7 tens, and 152 has 5 tens).

That is 12 tens. And, **10 tens makes a hundred!** So, we make a new hundred, and regroup that with the other hundreds, writing the new hundred with a little "1" in the hundreds column.

(We have 2 tens left over from that, and they stay in the tens column.)

1. Circle ten 10-sticks to make a new hundred. Write the addition.
   Alternatively, you can do these exercises using base-ten blocks or similar manipulatives.

a. | | | | | | | | + | | | | | _____ + _____ = _____	**b.** H H | | | | | | + | | | | | _____ + _____ = _____
c. H H | | | | H H | | | | + | | | | | _____ + _____ = _____	**d.** H | | | | H | | | + | | | | | | | | · · · · · _____ + _____ = _____
e. H H | | | | | | H H H | | . H + | | | | | | _____ + _____ = _____	**f.** H H | | | H H | | | + | | | | | | | | | H · · · · · · _____ + _____ = _____

2. Write the numbers in the grid, and add. Regroup. You can circle 10 ten-sticks in the picture to help you. Alternatively, you can do these exercises using base-ten blocks or similar manipulatives.

a.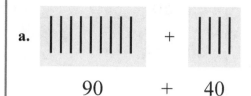

90   +   40

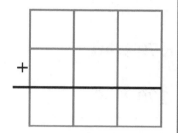

b.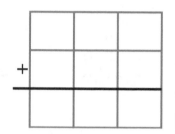

180   +   140

c.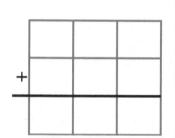

350   +   63

d.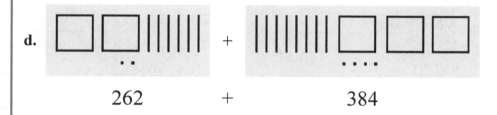

262   +   384

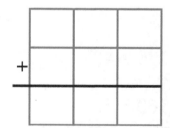

e.

370   +   345

3. Add mentally. Compare the problems. Notice you get a NEW hundred from the tens!

a.	b.	c.
70 + 40 = _____	50 + 60 = _____	90 + 50 = _____
170 + 40 = _____	150 + 60 = _____	290 + 50 = _____
270 + 40 = _____	250 + 60 = _____	490 + 50 = _____

4. Add. You need to regroup 10 tens as a new hundred.

a.
$$\begin{array}{r} 80 \\ + 30 \\ \hline \end{array}$$

b.
$$\begin{array}{r} 220 \\ + 90 \\ \hline \end{array}$$

c.
$$\begin{array}{r} 64 \\ + 53 \\ \hline \end{array}$$

d.
$$\begin{array}{r} 370 \\ + 74 \\ \hline \end{array}$$

e.
$$\begin{array}{r} 533 \\ + 282 \\ \hline \end{array}$$

f.
$$\begin{array}{r} 67 \\ + 72 \\ \hline \end{array}$$

g.
$$\begin{array}{r} 224 \\ + 193 \\ \hline \end{array}$$

h.
$$\begin{array}{r} 464 \\ + 392 \\ \hline \end{array}$$

i.
$$\begin{array}{r} 355 \\ + 374 \\ \hline \end{array}$$

j.
$$\begin{array}{r} 787 \\ + 82 \\ \hline \end{array}$$

5. Add mentally. THINK of the new hundred you might get from adding the tens.

a.	b.	c.
70 + 40 = _____	80 + 60 = _____	290 + 50 = _____
130 + 40 = _____	270 + 60 = _____	220 + 50 = _____
160 + 50 = _____	130 + 50 = _____	190 + 20 = _____

6. What number was added? Think of regrouping!

a.
$$\begin{array}{r} 167 \\ + 1\,\boxed{}\,2 \\ \hline 359 \end{array}$$

b.
$$\begin{array}{r} 240 \\ + 1\,\boxed{}\,2 \\ \hline 422 \end{array}$$

c.
$$\begin{array}{r} 391 \\ + 4\,\boxed{}\,2 \\ \hline 813 \end{array}$$

d.
$$\begin{array}{r} 653 \\ + 1\,\boxed{}\,3 \\ \hline 846 \end{array}$$

e.
$$\begin{array}{r} 375 \\ + 1\,\boxed{}\,4 \\ \hline 559 \end{array}$$

7. Add and match the letters with the answers in the key. The key then solves the riddle.

W	L	P	T	S
2 3 3 + 7 5 8	5 5 3 + 3 4 6	5 9 7 + 3 3 0	1 9 1 + 7 5 1	2 8 2 + 6 4 7
E	**O**	**A**	**E**	**I**
1 1 1 + 7 2 9	7 7 2 + 1 3 2	4 7 4 + 3 4 3	2 1 7 + 6 3 9	4 7 0 + 3 9 9
G	**N**	**R**	**F**	**H**
2 1 6 1 1 6 + 5 2 9	2 3 1 2 4 0 + 4 3 2	8 5 2 0 5 + 6 4 3	1 3 6 1 3 4 + 5 8 9	1 0 5 3 0 1 + 4 5 9

Key:

817	840	856	859	861	865	869	899	903	904	927	933	929	942	991

1. How do you put an elephant in the fridge?

   - You open the door, put the elephant in, and close the door. ☺

2. How do you put a giraffe in the fridge?

   - You open the door, take the elephant out, put the giraffe in, and close the door. ☺

3. When the elephant and the giraffe ran a race, who won?

942	865	840

856	899	856	927	865	817	903	942

, because

942	865	856

861	869	933	817	859	859	840

991	817	929

869	903

942	865	856

933	840	859	933	869	861	856	933	817	942	904	933

Add in Columns: Regrouping Twice

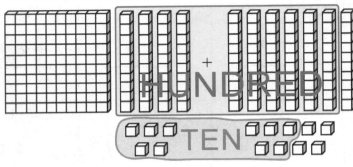

145 + 79

10 ones form a new ten. 10 tens form a new hundred.

The total is 224. Can you see that in the picture?

(You can also use manipulatives to do this problem.)

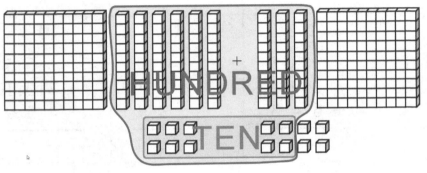

166 + 138

10 ones form a new ten. 10 tens form a new hundred.

The total is 304. Can you see that in the picture?

(You can also use manipulatives to do this problem.)

You have to regroup the ones and the tens. You have to regroup two times.

1. Circle ten 1-dots to make a new ten, AND circle ten 10-sticks to make a new hundred.
   Write the addition. Alternatively, you can do these exercises using base-ten blocks or similar manipulatives.

a. | | | | | + | | | | | | | |

. . . .

_____ + _____ = _____

b. | | | | | | | | + | | | | | | |

. . . .

_____ + _____ = _____

c. [H] | | | | | + | | | | | |

. . . .

_____ + _____ = _____

d. [H] | | | | | | + [H] | | |

. . . .

_____ + _____ = _____

	hundreds	tens	ones
	1	1	
	1	8	7
+	1	3	8
	3	2	5

Add in the ones column: $7 + 8 = 15$.
There are more than 10 ones, so regroup them as 1 ten 5 ones, writing "1" in the tens column.

Add in the tens column: $1 + 8 + 3 = 12$.
There are 10 tens, so regroup them as 1 hundred, writing "1" in the hundreds column.

2. Write the numbers in the grid, and add. Regroup. You can circle 10 ten-sticks AND 10 ones in the picture to help you. Alternatively, you can do these exercises using base-ten blocks or similar manipulatives.

a.  96 + 145

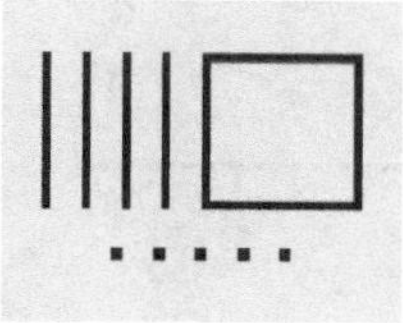

b.  185 + 157

c. 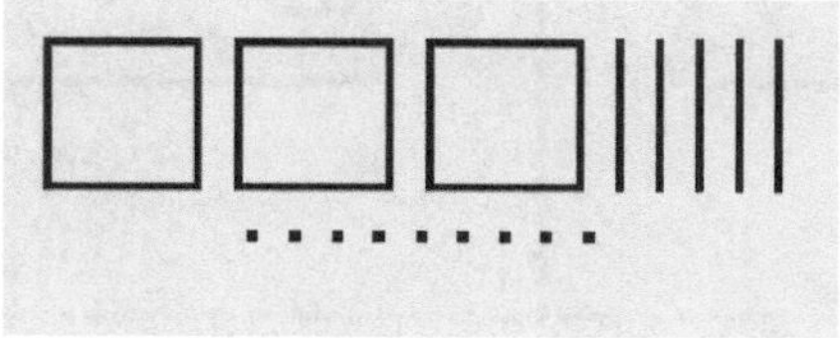 359 + 63

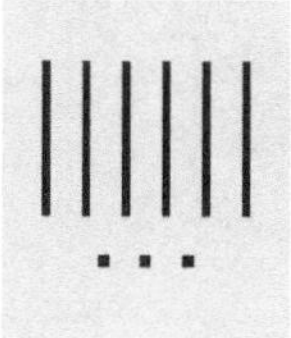

d.  267 + 385

3. Mary added 256 and 384 using the picture. Explain how she did it.

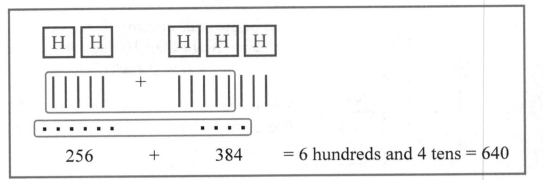

256 + 384 = 6 hundreds and 4 tens = 640

4. Add. Regroup two times if necessary.

a. 306 +461	**b.** 299 +225	**c.** 488 +322	**d.** 115 +536
e. 704 + 156	**f.** 260 + 341	**g.** 248 + 376	**h.** 173 + 646

i. 404
   199
+ 156
	j. 701
	   129
	+ 101
		k. 335
		   219
		+ 278
			l. 103
			   280
			+ 547

5. Matt solved 650 + 331 in an interesting way. Can you follow his thinking? Fill in.

First I check the hundreds: 600 + 300 makes _____.

Then I add the _____, and I get 50 + _____ = _____ .

Lastly in the ones, there's just 0 and 1, which is 1.

Okay, so I have these parts: 900, 80, and ____, so that makes _____.

90

6. Solve the word problems.

a. From Flowertown to Princetown is 148 miles.
You travel from Flowertown to Princetown
and back to Flowertown. How many miles is that?

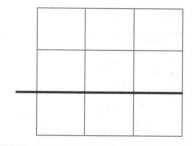

b. The school bought pencils for $128,
pens for $219, and notebooks for $549.
Find the total cost of the items.

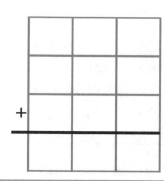

c. Find how many feet it is if you walk all of the way
around this triangle.

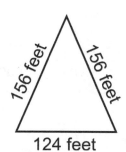

124 feet

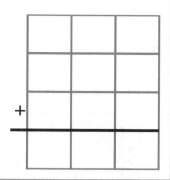

Puzzle Corner   What numbers are missing from the addition problems?

```
   □  3  □              2  □  □            1  6  9            □  8  8
 + 1  □  9            + □  3  6          + □  5  □          + 7  □  □
 ─────────            ─────────          ─────────          ─────────
   3  9  1              5  1  7            7  □  4            9  0  0
```

91

Regrouping in Subtraction, Part 1

We will now study regrouping ("borrowing") in subtraction.

As a first step, we study breaking a ten-pillar into ten little cubes. This is called **regrouping**, because one ten "changes groups" from the tens group into the ones.

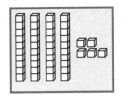

Break a ten.

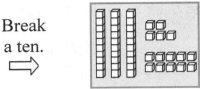

4 tens 5 ones

First we have 45. We "break" one ten-pillar into little cubes.

3 tens 15 ones

Now we have 3 tens and 15 ones. It is still 45, but written in a different way.

Here is another example. First we have 5 tens 3 ones. We "break" one ten-pillar into 10 little cubes. We end up with 4 tens 13 ones.

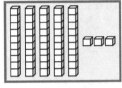

Break a ten.

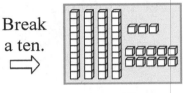

5 tens 3 ones   **4 tens 13 ones**

1. Break a ten into 10 ones. What do you get? Draw or use manipulatives to help.

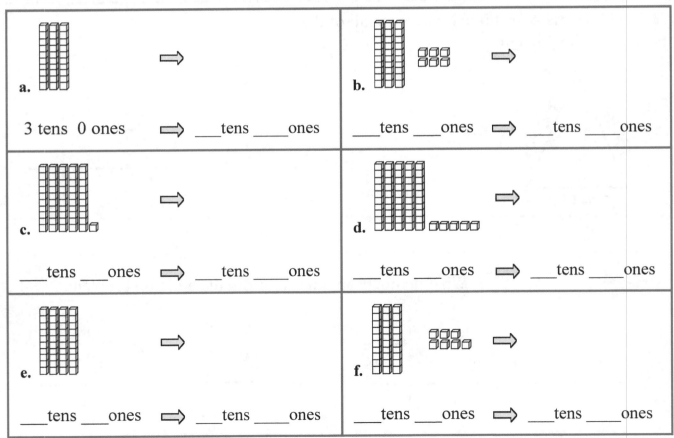

a.

3 tens 0 ones ⇒ ___tens ____ones

b.

___tens ____ones ⇒ ___tens ____ones

c.

___tens ___ones ⇒ ___tens ____ones

d.

___tens ___ones ⇒ ___tens ____ones

e.

___tens ___ones ⇒ ___tens ____ones

f.

___tens ___ones ⇒ ___tens ____ones

Let's study subtraction. The pictures on the right illustrate 45 – 17.

First, a ten is broken into 10 ones. So, 4 tens 5 ones becomes 3 tens 15 ones.

After that, cross out (subtract) 1 ten 7 ones.

4 tens 5 ones   Break a ten.   3 tens 15 ones

Cross out 1 ten 7 ones (from the *second* picture).

What is left? _____ tens _____ ones

The pictures on the right illustrate 52 – 39.

First, a ten is broken into 10 ones. So, 5 tens 2 ones becomes 4 tens 12 ones.

After that, cross out (subtract) 3 tens 9 ones.

5 tens 2 ones   Break a ten.   4 tens 12 ones

Cross out 3 tens 9 ones (from the *second* picture).

What is left? _____ tens _____ ones

---

2. Fill in. Always subtract (cross out some) from the *second* picture.

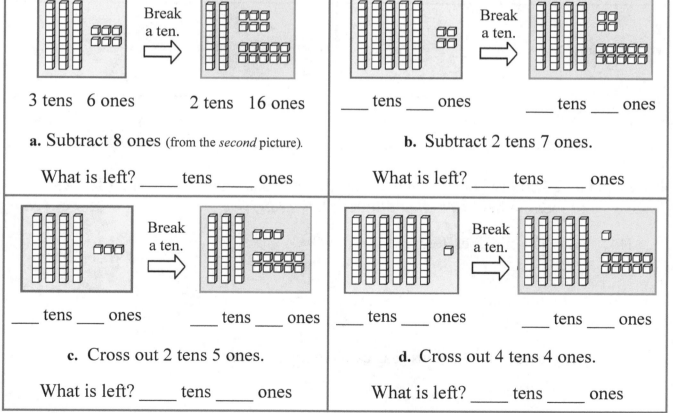

3 tens   6 ones   2 tens   16 ones

a. Subtract 8 ones (from the *second* picture).

What is left? _____ tens _____ ones

___ tens ___ ones   ___ tens ___ ones

b. Subtract 2 tens 7 ones.

What is left? _____ tens _____ ones

___ tens ___ ones   ___ tens ___ ones

c. Cross out 2 tens 5 ones.

What is left? _____ tens _____ ones

___ tens ___ ones   ___ tens ___ ones

d. Cross out 4 tens 4 ones.

What is left? _____ tens _____ ones

93

3. First, break a ten. Then subtract ones and tens separately. Look at the example.

a. 5 tens 5 ones ⟹ 4 tens 15 ones − 3 tens 7 ones ─────────── 1 ten 8 ones	**b.** 7 tens 2 ones ⟹ ___ tens ___ ones − 3 tens 5 ones ─────────── ___ tens ___ ones
c. 6 tens 0 ones ⟹ ___ tens ___ ones − 2 tens 7 ones ─────────── ___ tens ___ ones	**d.** 6 tens 4 ones ⟹ ___ tens ___ ones − 3 tens 8 ones ─────────── ___ tens ___ ones
e. 7 tens 6 ones ⟹ ___ tens ___ ones − 4 tens 7 ones ─────────── ___ tens ___ ones	**f.** 5 tens 0 ones ⟹ ___ tens ___ ones − 2 tens 2 ones ─────────── ___ tens ___ ones
g. 8 tens 1 one ⟹ ___ tens ___ ones − 6 tens 5 ones ─────────── ___ tens ___ ones	**h.** 6 tens 3 ones ⟹ ___ tens ___ ones − 2 tens 8 ones ─────────── ___ tens ___ ones

4. Jessica had 27 colored pencils and her brother and sister had none. Then Jessica gave 10 of them to her brother, and four to her sister.

   a. How many pencils does Jessica have now?

   b. How many more pencils does Jessica have than her brother?

   c. How many more pencils does Jessica have than her sister?

Regrouping in Subtraction, Part 2

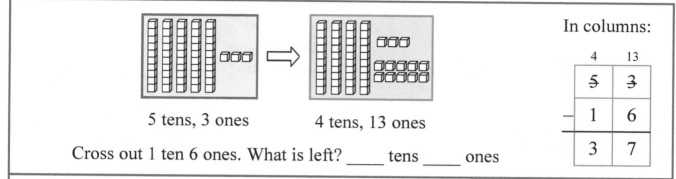

5 tens, 3 ones   4 tens, 13 ones

Cross out 1 ten 6 ones. What is left? _____ tens _____ ones

When the subtraction is done *in columns*:

- We take (borrow) one ten from the 5 tens. There will be now only 4 tens in the tens column, so to show this, we **cross the "5"** in the tens column and **write 4 above it**.

- This new ten is now grouped with the ones. There were 3 ones, but with the 10 new ones there will be 13. To show this, we also **cross the "3"** in the ones column and **write 13 above it**.

- Then we subtract the tens and ones separately.

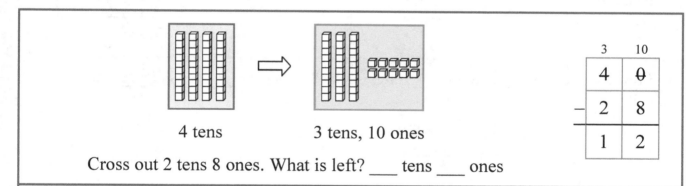

4 tens   3 tens, 10 ones

Cross out 2 tens 8 ones. What is left? ___ tens ___ ones

Here is another example: 40 – 28.

- We take (borrow) one ten from the 4 tens. There will be now only 3 tens in the tens column, so to show this, we **cross the "4"** in the tens column and **write 3 above it**.

- This new ten is now grouped with the ones. There were 0 ones, but with the 10 new ones there will be 10. To show this, we also **cross the "0"** in the ones column and **write 10 above it**.

- Then we subtract the tens and ones separately in columns.

1. Regroup first. Then subtract.

a. 6 tens 0 ones → _____ tens _____ ones

Take away
3 tens, 9 ones.

	6	0
−	3	9

b. 7 tens 1 one → _____ tens _____ ones

Take away
1 ten, 6 ones.

	7	1
−	1	6

c. 3 tens, 5 ones → _____ tens _____ ones

Take away
1 ten, 7 ones.

	3	5
−	1	7

d. 8 tens → _____ tens _____ ones

Take away
3 tens, 4 ones.

	8	0
−	3	4

e. 7 tens, 6 ones → _____ tens _____ ones

Take away
4 tens, 8 ones.

	7	6
−	4	8

f. 9 tens → _____ tens _____ ones

Take away
5 tens, 1 one.

	9	0
−	5	1

g. 5 tens, 4 ones → _____ tens _____ ones

Take away
2 tens, 5 ones.

−		

h. 8 tens → _____ tens _____ ones

Take away
4 tens, 7 ones.

−		

i. 7 tens, 4 ones → _____ tens _____ ones

Take away
3 tens, 8 ones.

−		

j. 4 tens 7 ones → _____ tens _____ ones

Take away
2 tens, 9 ones.

−		

2. Subtract. Check by adding the result and what was subtracted.

a. $\begin{array}{r} {}^{4}\!\!\!\!\;{}^{16}\\ \cancel{5}\;\cancel{6}\\ -\;2\;7\\ \hline 2\;9 \end{array}$ Check: $\begin{array}{r} {}^{1}\\ 2\;9\\ +\;2\;7\\ \hline 5\;6 \end{array}$	**b.** $\begin{array}{r} 9\;0\\ -\;2\;8\\ \hline \end{array}$ Check: $\begin{array}{r} +\;2\;8\\ \hline \end{array}$	**c.** $\begin{array}{r} 4\;2\\ -\;1\;5\\ \hline \end{array}$ Check: $\begin{array}{r} +\;1\;5\\ \hline \end{array}$
d. $\begin{array}{r} 9\;0\\ -\;3\;5\\ \hline \end{array}$	**e.** $\begin{array}{r} 8\;2\\ -\;2\;5\\ \hline \end{array}$	**f.** $\begin{array}{r} 6\;5\\ -\;3\;9\\ \hline \end{array}$
g. $\begin{array}{r} 5\;2\\ -\;1\;4\\ \hline \end{array}$	**h.** $\begin{array}{r} 6\;5\\ -\;2\;6\\ \hline \end{array}$	**i.** $\begin{array}{r} 7\;0\\ -\;4\;8\\ \hline \end{array}$
j. $\begin{array}{r} 5\;5\\ -\;1\;7\\ \hline \end{array}$	**k.** $\begin{array}{r} 3\;1\\ -\;1\;8\\ \hline \end{array}$	**l.** $\begin{array}{r} 6\;6\\ -\;2\;8\\ \hline \end{array}$

Figure out the missing numbers in these subtractions! You might need to regroup.

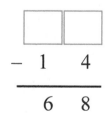

Puzzle Corner

$\begin{array}{r} \square\;3\\ -\;1\;\square\\ \hline 7\;5 \end{array}$ $\quad$ $\begin{array}{r} 8\;\square\\ -\;\square\;7\\ \hline 1\;6 \end{array}$ $\quad$ $\begin{array}{r} \square\;0\\ -\;3\;\square\\ \hline 4\;2 \end{array}$ $\quad$ $\begin{array}{r} \square\;\square\\ -\;1\;4\\ \hline 6\;8 \end{array}$ $\quad$ $\begin{array}{r} 6\;2\\ -\;\square\;\square\\ \hline 5\;3 \end{array}$

Regrouping in Subtraction, Part 3

Sometimes we need to regroup in subtraction, and sometimes not. Check carefully in the ones column. Are there enough ones to do the subtraction, or not? If not, you need to regroup.	Do you need to regroup? YES / NO	$\begin{array}{r} 6\ 1 \\ -\ 2\ 6 \\ \hline \end{array}$	Do you need to regroup? YES / NO	$\begin{array}{r} 7\ 4 \\ -\ 2\ 3 \\ \hline \end{array}$

1. Look at the ones' digits. Do you need to regroup (borrow a ten in the ones' column)?

a. Do you need to regroup? YES / NO	$\begin{array}{r} 5\ 4 \\ -\ 3\ 2 \\ \hline \end{array}$	**b.** Do you need to regroup? YES / NO	$\begin{array}{r} 5\ 0 \\ -\ 2\ 5 \\ \hline \end{array}$	**c.** Do you need to regroup? YES / NO	$\begin{array}{r} 8\ 2 \\ -\ 5\ 6 \\ \hline \end{array}$

2. Subtract. Regroup if necessary. Find the answers in the line of numbers below.

a. Do you need to regroup? YES / NO	$\begin{array}{r} 6\ 0 \\ -\ 1\ 6 \\ \hline \end{array}$	**b.** Do you need to regroup? YES / NO	$\begin{array}{r} 5\ 7 \\ -\ 3\ 2 \\ \hline \end{array}$	**c.** Do you need to regroup? YES / NO	$\begin{array}{r} 4\ 3 \\ -\ 1\ 7 \\ \hline \end{array}$
d. $\begin{array}{r} 8\ 0 \\ -\ 2\ 8 \\ \hline \end{array}$	**e.** $\begin{array}{r} 9\ 7 \\ -\ 2\ 5 \\ \hline \end{array}$	**f.** $\begin{array}{r} 8\ 1 \\ -\ 5\ 7 \\ \hline \end{array}$	**g.** $\begin{array}{r} 3\ 7 \\ -\ 2\ 7 \\ \hline \end{array}$	**h.** $\begin{array}{r} 6\ 0 \\ -\ 4\ 1 \\ \hline \end{array}$

44 26 19 25 24 72 10 52 25

3. Subtract mentally.

a. $64 - 20 =$ _____	**b.** $77 - 71 =$ _____	**c.** $98 - 6 =$ _____
$98 - 50 =$ _____	$45 - 40 =$ _____	$50 - 46 =$ _____

The number line arrows illustrate the subtraction 23 − 7. The first, red, arrow goes from 0 to 23. The second, blue, arrow goes 7 steps backwards from 23 and ends at 16.

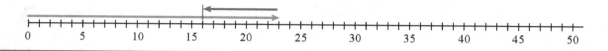

4. Write the subtractions illustrated by the arrows on the number line.

a.

b.

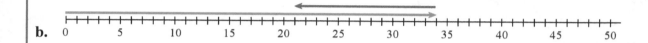

c.

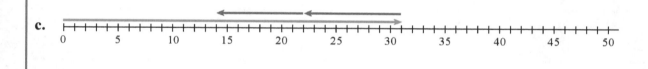

5. Draw arrows to illustrate these subtractions on the number line.

a. 22 − 9 = _____

b. 36 − 12 = _____

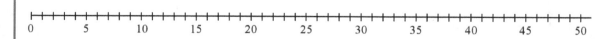

c. 44 − 17 = _____

Remember, subtraction and addition are connected. For example, 9 − 4 = 5 and 5 + 4 = 9.

You can use this connection, and <u>check</u> each subtraction by adding.

Add the answer you got *and* the number you subtracted. You should get the number you subtracted from.

For example, to check if 68 − 45 is really 23, add 23 + 45 and check if you get 68.

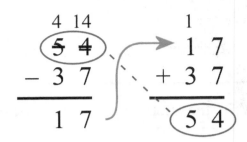

6. Subtract. Regroup if necessary. Check each subtraction by *adding your answer and the number you subtracted.*

a.		b.	
$\begin{array}{r} \overset{8\ \ 14}{9\ 4} \\ -\ 3\ 5 \\ \hline 5\ 9 \end{array}$ $\begin{array}{r} 5\ 9 \\ +\ 3\ 5 \\ \hline \end{array}$		$\begin{array}{r} 8\ 2 \\ -\ 2\ 5 \\ \hline \end{array}$ $\begin{array}{r} \\ +\ 2\ 5 \\ \hline \end{array}$	
c.		d.	
$\begin{array}{r} 6\ 1 \\ -\ 4\ 9 \\ \hline \end{array}$ $\begin{array}{r} \\ +\ 4\ 9 \\ \hline \end{array}$		$\begin{array}{r} 9\ 9 \\ -\ 5\ 7 \\ \hline \end{array}$ $\begin{array}{r} \\ +\ 5\ 7 \\ \hline \end{array}$	
e.		f.	
$\begin{array}{r} 6\ 0 \\ -\ 2\ 3 \\ \hline \end{array}$ $\begin{array}{r} \\ +\ 2\ 3 \\ \hline \end{array}$		$\begin{array}{r} 6\ 6 \\ -\ 4\ 8 \\ \hline \end{array}$ $\begin{array}{r} \\ +\ 4\ 8 \\ \hline \end{array}$	
g.		h.	
$\begin{array}{r} 5\ 4 \\ -\ 4\ 1 \\ \hline \end{array}$ $\begin{array}{r} \\ +\quad\quad \\ \hline \end{array}$		$\begin{array}{r} 8\ 5 \\ -\ 3\ 9 \\ \hline \end{array}$ $\begin{array}{r} \\ +\quad\quad \\ \hline \end{array}$	

7. Solve. IF you subtract, check the answer by adding
   (you will not subtract in every problem).

a. Emily picked 29 rows of strawberries
and Jim picked 13 rows of strawberries.
How many more rows of strawberries
did Emily pick?

b. Judith sold 35 tickets for the county fair
and Peter sold 62 tickets. How many
more tickets did Peter sell than Judith?

c. Judith sold 35 tickets for the county fair
and Peter sold 62 tickets. How many
tickets did they sell together?

d. A pretty doll with a blue dress costs $28,
and a different doll with a pink dress
costs $12 more than that. How much
does that doll cost?

e. Bill bought two bicycle chains for $18 each and
a saddle for $49. How much was the total cost?

Word Problems

"More" in word problems

Study carefully these problems. They all use the word MORE, but they are different!
Solve each problem with your teacher or on your own, if you can. In each problem
think first, "WHO has more?" (If the problems are difficult, drawing illustrations for the situations
may help.)

- Anna has 12 sheep. Her neighbor has 7 more sheep than Anna.
  How many sheep does the neighbor have?

- Anna has 7 more sheep than her neighbor. Anna has 12 sheep.
  How many sheep does the neighbor have?

- Anna has 12 sheep, and her neighbor has 7.
  How many more sheep does Anna have than her neighbor?

1. Solve. Think if you need addition or subtraction.

a. Isabella has a flock of 15 goats. Her neighbor Andy has 18 goats.
How many more goats does Andy have than Isabella?

b. Isabella has a flock of 15 goats. Her neighbor Sandy has 8 more goats
than Isabella. How many goats does Sandy have?

c. Isabella has 15 goats, which is 5 more than what Henry has.
How many goats does Henry have?

d. Christopher has 27 cows, and Daniel has 16 more than that.
How many cows does Daniel have?

"Fewer" (or "less") in word problems

FEWER is the opposite of MORE. These three problems all use the word FEWER, but they are different! Solve each problem with your teacher or on your own, if you can. In each problem **think** first, "WHO has more?"

- Anna has 12 sheep. Her neighbor has 7 fewer sheep than Anna.
  How many sheep does the neighbor have?

- Anna has 7 fewer sheep than her neighbor. Anna has 12 sheep.
  How many sheep does the neighbor have?

- Anna has 7 sheep, and her neighbor has 12.
  How many fewer sheep does Anna have than her neighbor?

2. Solve. Think if you need addition or subtraction.

a. Joe has 27 tennis balls and Mason has 5 fewer tennis balls than Joe. How many tennis balls does Mason have?

b. Joe has 27 tennis balls, which is 7 less than what Logan has. How many tennis balls does Logan have?

c. Liz wants to buy a blue dress that costs $41.
A white dress, costs $13 less than that.
And a yellow dress costs $3 less than the white dress.

How much does the yellow dress cost?

d. Find how much it is if Liz buys both the blue and the yellow dress.

3. Subtract mentally.

a. 30 − 28 = _____	**d.** 70 − 63 = _____	**g.** 56 − 5 = _____
b. 52 − 30 = _____	**e.** 70 − 6 = _____	**h.** 18 − 7 = _____
c. 98 − 90 = _____	**f.** 100 − 5 = _____	**i.** 46 − 4 = _____

4. Solve. You may need to both add and subtract.

a. Ryan rode his horse for 11 km each day for two days. Zoe rode her horse for 8 km each day for two days.

In two days, how many kilometers less did Zoe ride hers than what Ryan rode his?

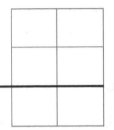 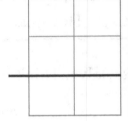

b. Mia owns 32 dolls and her friend Ava has less. Actually, Ava has 8 fewer dolls than Mia. How many dolls do the girls have in total?

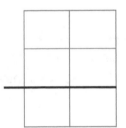 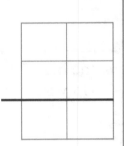

Puzzle Corner Find out what number the triangle means. You are solving *equations*!

a. 63 + △ = 71	**b.** 80 − △ = 54	**c.** △ − 10 = 40
△ = _____	△ = _____	△ = _____

Write your own "triangle problems" (equations), and let a friend solve them.

d.	**e.**	**f.**
△ = _____	△ = _____	△ = _____

Mental Subtraction, Part 1

<table>
<tr><td colspan="2"><u>Method 1:</u>   Subtract in two parts</td></tr>
</table>

$$53 - \underline{8}$$
$$= 53 - \underline{3} - \underline{5}$$
$$= \quad 50 \quad - 5 = 45$$

Subtract 8 in two parts: first 3, then 5.

$$72 - \underline{6}$$
$$= 72 - \underline{2} - \underline{4}$$
$$= \quad 70 \quad - 4 = 66$$

Subtract 6 in two parts: first 2, then 4.

In other words, first subtract to the *previous whole ten*, then the rest.

1. Subtract the elevated number in parts. (First subtract to the previous whole ten; then the rest.)

<table>
<tr>
<td>

$- 5$
/ \\

a. $51 - \underline{1} - \underline{4} =$ _____
</td>
<td>

$- 7$
/ \\

b. $62 -$ ____ $-$ ____ $=$ _____
</td>
</tr>
<tr>
<td>

$- 4$
/ \\

c. $33 -$ ____ $-$ ____ $=$ _____
</td>
<td>

$- 5$
/ \\

d. $92 -$ ____ $-$ ____ $=$ _____
</td>
</tr>
<tr>
<td>

$- 6$
/ \\

e. $75 -$ ____ $-$ ____ $=$ _____
</td>
<td>

$- 7$
/ \\

f. $63 -$ ____ $-$ ____ $=$ _____
</td>
</tr>
<tr>
<td>

$- 7$
/ \\

g. $35 -$ ____ $-$ ____ $=$ _____
</td>
<td>

$- 5$
/ \\

h. $74 -$ ____ $-$ ____ $=$ _____
</td>
</tr>
</table>

2. First subtract the balls that are not in the ten-groups.

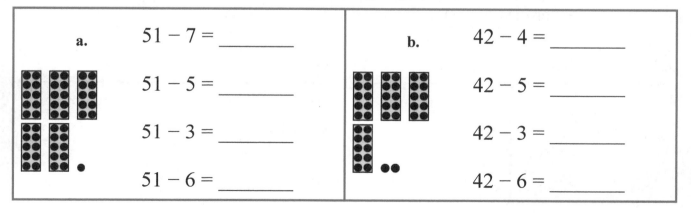

a.
$51 - 7 =$ _____
$51 - 5 =$ _____
$51 - 3 =$ _____
$51 - 6 =$ _____

b.
$42 - 4 =$ _____
$42 - 5 =$ _____
$42 - 3 =$ _____
$42 - 6 =$ _____

Method 2: Use known subtraction facts
Since $14 - 6 = 8$, we know that the answer to $74 - 6$ will end in 8, but it will be in the sixties sixty-something. So it is 68.
Since $15 - 8 = 7$, we know that the answer to $55 - 8$ will end in 7, but it will be in the forties forty-something. So it is 47.

3. Subtract. The first problem in each box is a "helping problem" for the others.

a. $14 - 9 =$ _____ $24 - 9 =$ _____ $44 - 9 =$ _____	b. $17 - 8 =$ _____ $27 - 8 =$ _____ $37 - 8 =$ _____	c. $12 - 9 =$ _____ $52 - 9 =$ _____ $32 - 9 =$ _____
d. $15 - 9 =$ _____ $65 - 9 =$ _____ $45 - 9 =$ _____	e. $13 - 8 =$ _____ $33 - 8 =$ _____ $93 - 8 =$ _____	f. $16 - 8 =$ _____ $86 - 8 =$ _____ $36 - 8 =$ _____

4. a. Amy has \$32. She bought a comic book for \$7.
How much does she have now?

   b. Peter had \$29. A toy train he wants costs \$39.
Mom paid him \$5 for working. How much more
does Peter now need to buy the train?

   c. A flower shop has 55 roses. Eight of them are white,
and the rest are red. How many are red?

5. Use either method from this lesson to subtract.

a.	b.	c.	d.
$34 - 5 =$ ____	$65 - 9 =$ ____	$51 - 8 =$ ____	$62 - 7 =$ ____
$73 - 7 =$ ____	$36 - 8 =$ ____	$93 - 6 =$ ____	$83 - 8 =$ ____

Mental Subtraction, Part 2

Method 3:   Add.
You can "add backwards". This works well if the two numbers are close to each other.
Instead of subtracting, think how much you need to add to the number being subtracted (the subtrahend) in order to get the number you are subtracting from (the minuend).

Think: 84 + ▢ = 92 $\quad$ +▢▢	Think: 25 + ▢ = 75 $\quad$ +▢
(84 and how many more makes 92?) $\qquad$ 92 − 84 = _____	(25 and how many more makes 75?) $\qquad$ 75 − 25 = _____

1. To find these differences, think of adding more.

+ 8	+ ___	+ ___
a. 92 − 84 = _____	**b.** 51 − 49 = _____	**c.** 76 − 69 = _____
(Think: 84 + ____ = 92)	(Think: 49 + ___ = 51)	(Think: 69 + ___ = 76)
d. 32 − 28 = _____	**g.** 90 − 83 = _____	**j.** 100 − 95 = _____
e. 22 − 14 = _____	**h.** 64 − 56 = _____	**k.** 64 − 55 = _____
f. 53 − 46 = _____	**i.** 72 − 65 = _____	**l.** 44 − 37 = _____

2. Solve. Think if you need addition or subtraction—or both.

a. Jerry has 46 toy cars. Larry has 7 more than Jerry, and Mickey has 7 less than Jerry. How many toy cars does Larry have?   And Mickey?
b. Andy has $33. He bought a gift for his mom that cost $28. Then, Andy got $5 from his dad for helping with car repairs. How much money does Andy have now?

Method 4: Subtract in parts: tens and ones

Break the number being subtracted into its tens and ones. Subtract in parts.

$$53 - \boxed{21}$$
$$= 53 - \boxed{20} - \underline{1}$$
$$= \quad 33 \quad - 1 = 32$$

First subtract 20, then 1.

$$87 - \boxed{46}$$
$$= 87 - \underline{40} - \underline{6}$$
$$= \quad 47 \quad - 6 = 41$$

First subtract 40, then 6.

3. Solve.

a. $78 - 22$	**b.** $56 - 31$	**c.** $46 - 25$
THINK: $78 - 20 - 2$	THINK: $56 - 30 - 1$	$46 - \underline{} - \underline{}$
= _____	= _____	= _____
d. $66 - 43$	**e.** $28 - 12$	**f.** $84 - 52$
$66 - \underline{} - \underline{}$	$28 - \underline{} - \underline{}$	$84 - \underline{} - \underline{}$
= _____	= _____	= _____
g. $99 - 66 =$ _____	**h.** $47 - 34 =$ _____	**i.** $78 - 67 =$ _____

4. **a.** Noah counted books on his bookshelf. One shelf had 34 books. Another had 42. How many more books did that shelf have than the first?

   b. Noah took four books from the second shelf and put them on the first one. Now how many more books does the second shelf have than the first?

5. Draw arrows to illustrate the subtraction on the number line.

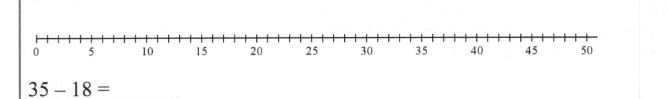

$35 - 18 =$ _____

Method 5: Subtract in parts: tens and ones

Break BOTH the number you subtract from AND the number being subtracted into its tens and ones. Subtract the tens. Subtract the ones.

53 – 21	76 – 33
$= 50 - 20$ and $3 - 1$	$= 70 - 30$ and $6 - 3$
$=$ 30 and 2 $=$ 32	$=$ 40 and 3 $=$ 43

6. Solve.

a. $67 - 53$	**b.** $92 - 31$	**c.** $85 - 22$
$60 - 50$ and $7 - 3$ $=$ _____	$90 - 30$ and $2 - 1$ $=$ _____	$80 - 20$ and ___ – ___ $=$ _____
d. $88 - 62 =$ _____	**e.** $57 - 23 =$ _____	**f.** $79 - 17 =$ _____

7. **a.** Terry is on page 52 of her book. The book has a total of 95 pages. How many pages does she have left to read?

   b. Terry reads nine pages more. Now how many pages does she have left to read?

8. Devise your own method for these subtractions. Explain how your method works.

a. $52 - 36$	**b.** $81 - 47$

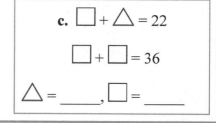

Puzzle Corner   The triangle and square represent "mystery numbers." Find them. Guess and check! Then change your guess.

a. $\triangle + \triangle + 10 = 34$ $\triangle =$ _____	**b.** $\square + \triangle = 22$ $\square - \triangle = 4$ $\triangle =$ ___ , $\square =$ ___	**c.** $\square + \triangle = 22$ $\square + \square = 36$ $\triangle =$ ___ , $\square =$ ___

Regrouping One Ten as Ten Ones
with 3-Digit Numbers

You have already learned how to regroup one ten as ten ones (borrow a ten) with two-digit numbers. It happens the same way with three-digit numbers.

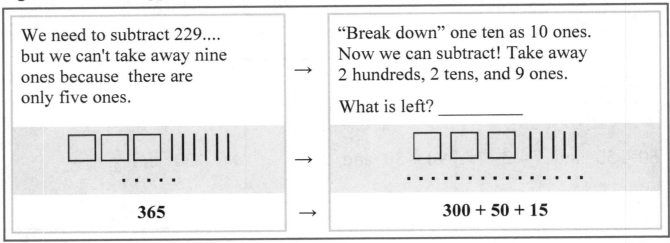

We need to subtract 229.... but we can't take away nine ones because there are only five ones.

365

→

"Break down" one ten as 10 ones. Now we can subtract! Take away 2 hundreds, 2 tens, and 9 ones.

What is left? _____

300 + 50 + 15

1. Break down ONE ten into ten ones (regroup). Draw squares for hundreds, sticks for tens, and dots for ones. Then take away (subtract) what is asked.

a. 341 → 300 + 30 + 11

Take away 127. What is left? _____

b. 425 → 400 + _____ + _____

Take away 218. What is left? _____

c. 267 → 200 + _____ + _____

Take away 139. What is left? _____

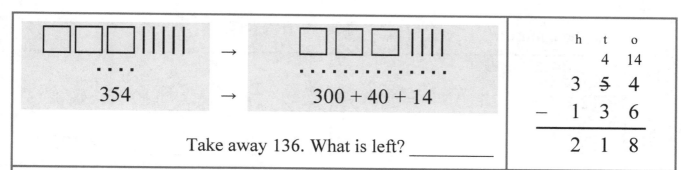

		h	t	o
			4	14
		3	~~5~~	4
	−	1	3	6
		2	1	8

354 → 300 + 40 + 14

Take away 136. What is left? _____

COMPARE the regrouping process in the pictures and how it is written in columns. It happens the same way as with two-digit numbers: Instead of 5 tens and 4 ones, we write 4 tens and 14 ones. Then we can subtract in the ones column.

2. Subtract. Regroup in the tens.

a.
```
  8 6 1
−   4 6
───────
```

b.
```
  5 9 2
− 1 2 5
───────
```

c.
```
  7 7 3
− 3 5 6
───────
```

3. Subtract. Regroup if necessary. Check each subtraction by *adding your answer and the number you subtracted.*

a.
```
    1 13
  8 2 3        6 1 8
− 2 0 5      + 2 0 5
───────      ───────
  6 1 8
```

b.
```
  6 7 1
− 4 5 5        + 4 5 5
───────        ───────
```

c.
```
  4 2 0
− 1 1 5        +
───────        ───────
```

d.
```
  5 1 6
− 2 0 8        +
───────        ───────
```

e.
```
  7 3 3
− 6 2 7        +
───────        ───────
```

f.
```
  6 8 7
− 3 0 9        +
───────        ───────
```

4. Continue the patterns.

a.	b.
120 + 120 = 240	1 + 119 = 120
121 + _____ = 240	2 + _____ = 120
122 + _____ = 240	3 + _____ = 120
_____ + _____ = 240	_____ + _____ = 120
_____ + _____ = 240	_____ + _____ = 120
_____ + _____ = 240	_____ + _____ = 120
_____ + _____ = 240	_____ + _____ = 120
_____ + _____ = 240	_____ + _____ = 120
_____ + _____ = 240	_____ + _____ = 120
THINK: How long can you continue this pattern?	THINK: How long can you continue this pattern?

5. Solve the problems.

a. There are 365 days in one year. How many days are there in two years?	b. Jack's family is driving from Easttown to Middletown, (a distance of 173 km). They have driven 69 km. How far do they still have to go?	c. Mike is on page 235 of his book. The book has 581 pages. How many pages does he still have to read?
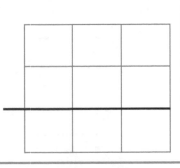		

Regrouping One Hundred As 10 Tens

We need to subtract 170.... but we cannot take away seven tens because there are only two tens.

→

"Break down" one HUNDRED as 10 tens. Now we can subtract! Take away 1 hundred and 7 tens.

What is left? _____

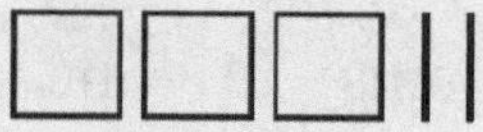

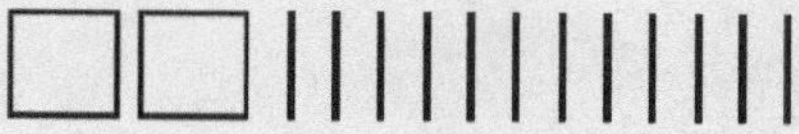

320 → → **2 hundreds + 12 tens**

1. Break down one hundred into 10 tens (regroup). Draw squares for hundreds, sticks for tens, and dots for ones. Then take away (subtract) what is asked.

a.

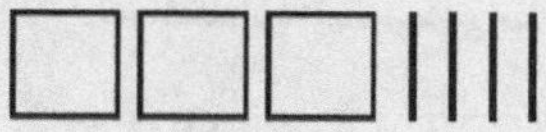

340 → →

_____ hundreds + _____ tens

Take away 180. What is left? _____

b.

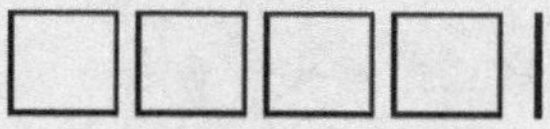

410 → →

_____ hundreds + _____ tens

Take away 250. What is left? _____

c.

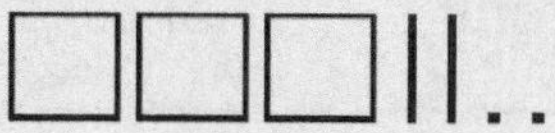

322 → →

_____ hundreds + _____ tens + _____ ones

Take away 171. What is left? _____

d.

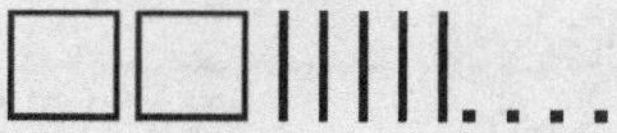

254 → →

_____ hundreds + _____ tens + _____ ones

Take away 174. What is left? _____

2. First, regroup 1 hundred as ten tens. Then subtract.

a. 4 hundreds 5 tens 7 ones ⟹

	3	15 tens	7 ones
−	2 hundreds	8 tens	2 ones
	1	7 tens	5 ones

b. 7 hundreds 2 tens 1 one ⟹

	hundreds	tens	one
−	3 hundreds	6 tens	1 one
	hundred	tens	ones

c. 3 hundreds 2 tens 0 ones ⟹

	hundreds	tens	ones
−	2 hundreds	5 tens	0 ones
	hundred	tens	ones

d. 7 hundreds 0 tens 6 ones ⟹

	hundreds	tens	ones
−	6 hundreds	2 tens	2 ones
	hundred	tens	ones

e. 8 hundreds 0 tens 3 ones ⟹

	hundreds	tens	ones
−	5 hundreds	3 tens	1 one
	hundred	tens	ones

3. How to regroup when subtracting 947 − 282 (below)? Fill in Jill's explanation.

It would be easy, except I cannot subtract ____ tens from ____ tens. So, I need to take one of the ____ hundreds and break it down as tens. So, now I will have only ____ hundreds but I will now get ___ tens. Now I can subtract.

9 hundreds 4 tens 7 ones ⟹

	hundreds	tens	ones
−	2 hundreds	8 tens	2 ones
	hundred	tens	ones

Compare how we write the regrouping when subtracting in columns.		
5 hundreds 4 tens 7 ones $\Longrightarrow$	**4** hundreds **14** tens **7** ones $-$ 1 hundred 5 tens 2 ones **3** hundreds **9** tens **5** ones	$\begin{array}{r} 4\ \ 14 \\ \cancel{5}\ 4\ 7 \\ -\ 1\ 5\ 2 \\ \hline 3\ 9\ 5 \end{array}$

4. Fill in. Subtract both ways.

a.

4 hundreds 5 tens 6 ones $\Longrightarrow$ ☐ hundreds ☐ tens ☐ ones

$-$ 2 hundreds   7 tens   2 ones

☐ hundreds ☐ tens ☐ ones

$\begin{array}{r} 4\ 5\ 6 \\ -\ 2\ 7\ 2 \\ \hline \end{array}$

b.

6 hundreds 0 tens 5 ones $\Longrightarrow$ ☐ hundreds ☐ tens ☐ ones

$-$ 4 hundreds   3 tens   3 ones

☐ hundreds ☐ tens ☐ ones

$\begin{array}{r} 6\ 0\ 5 \\ -\ 4\ 3\ 3 \\ \hline \end{array}$

5. Subtract.

a. $\begin{array}{r} 9\ 2\ 6 \\ -\ 1\ 4\ 6 \\ \hline \end{array}$	**b.** $\begin{array}{r} 5\ 2\ 9 \\ -\ \ \ 9\ 5 \\ \hline \end{array}$	**c.** $\begin{array}{r} 4\ 1\ 4 \\ -\ 3\ 2\ 2 \\ \hline \end{array}$	**d.** $\begin{array}{r} 7\ 7\ 3 \\ -\ 5\ 3\ 6 \\ \hline \end{array}$
e. $\begin{array}{r} 6\ 7\ 0 \\ -\ 2\ 2\ 6 \\ \hline \end{array}$	**f.** $\begin{array}{r} 7\ 0\ 8 \\ -\ 1\ 5\ 6 \\ \hline \end{array}$	**g.** $\begin{array}{r} 5\ 0\ 3 \\ -\ 3\ 4\ 1 \\ \hline \end{array}$	**h.** $\begin{array}{r} 7\ 4\ 8 \\ -\ 3\ 7\ 6 \\ \hline \end{array}$

6. Solve the problems.

a. Max has two books to read. The first book has 270 pages, and the second book has 60 fewer pages than the first. How many pages does the second book have?

b. Liz and Hannah played a game. Hannah got 192 points and Liz got 433 points. How many more points did Liz get than Hannah?

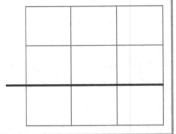

c. Again, Liz and Hannah played a game. This time Liz got 215 points and Hannah got 93 points more than Liz. So, how many points did Hannah get?

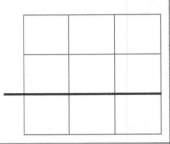

d. Denny and Micah dug up some worms for bait before they went fishing. Denny got 14 worms, which was 11 fewer worms than what Micah got. How many worms did Micah get?

What was the total number of worms that both boys got?

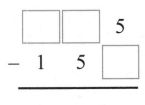 Figure out the missing numbers in these subtractions! You might need to regroup.

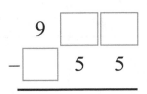

		5
− 1	5	
2	9	2

6		4
−	5	
3	2	6

9		
−	5	5
7	2	6

9	6	
−	5	5
5		5

Graphs and Problems

1. The table lists the eye colors of some children. Draw the bars for the bar graph.

9	4	10	16	11
blue	green	gray	brown	hazel

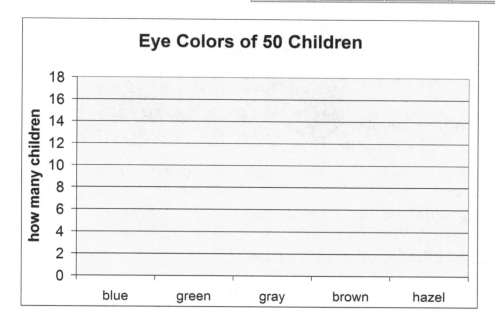

Eye Colors of 50 Children

a. How many children have either brown or hazel eyes?

b. How many more children have brown eyes than have green eyes?

c. How many children do not have blue eyes?

2. Solve the word problems. Add or subtract in columns if you need to.

a. Jim has 62 marbles, Peter has 28, and Ed has 33 marbles. Peter and Ed put their marbles together. Now do they have more than Jim?	**b.** You were on page 48 in a book that has a total of 95 pages. Then you read 10 more pages. How many pages have you read now?

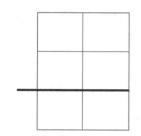

How many pages do you have left to read?

3. The bar graph below tells us the counts for different kinds of animals in a zoo. Answer the questions. Use the grids for additions and subtractions if you need to.

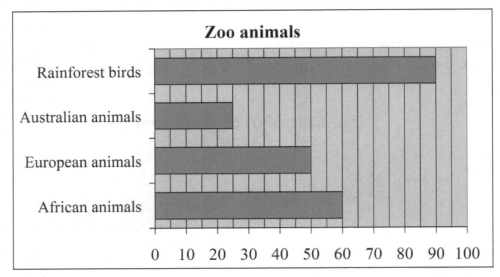

a. How many rainforest birds does the zoo have?

b. How many Australian animals are there?

c. How many Australian and African animals does the zoo have together?

d. How many more African animals does the zoo have than Australian animals?

e. How many Australian, European, and African animals are there?

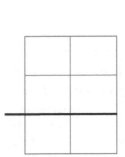 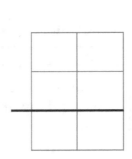 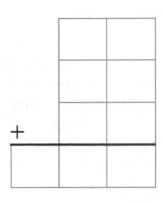

4. Break the number you are subtracting into tens and ones, and subtract in parts.

a. 45 − 23	b. 76 − 15	c. 47 − 15
/ \ 45 − 20 − 3 = _____	/ \ 76 − 10 − 5 = _____	

Euclid's Game

Euclid's game is simple, fun, and lets you practice finding the difference of two numbers!

> **Rules:**
>
> 1. The first player chooses *any number* on the 100-chart and circles or colors it.
> 2. The next player chooses *any other number* on the 100-chart and circles or colors it.
>
> After this, the numbers get marked by crossing them out.
>
> During his turn, each player has to find the *difference* of any two numbers already marked, and mark that number. The player can choose *any* two numbers for this; they just have to be already marked numbers.
>
> The player who cannot find any more numbers to mark is the loser.

Use the 100-chart on the next page as a game board. You can print it again for every new game. Alternatively, you may write the 100-chart on paper, of course.

Example. Initially Jane chooses 28 and Joe chooses 9. After that:

Jane: I mark 19 since it is the difference of 28 and 9.
Joe: I mark 10 since it is the difference of 19 and 9.
Jane: I mark 18 since it is the difference of 28 and 10.
Joe: I mark 1 since it is the difference of 19 and 18.
... and so on.

You may continue Jane's and Joe's play if you wish.

Eventually you should see all of the numbers from 1 to 28 marked, with Jane as the loser.

~~1~~	2	3	4	5	6	7	8	9	~~10~~
11	12	13	14	15	16	17	~~18~~	~~19~~	20
21	22	23	24	25	26	27	28	29	30
31	32	33	34	35	36	37	38	39	40
41	42	43	44	45	46	47	48	49	50
51	52	53	54	55	56	57	58	59	60
61	62	63	64	65	66	67	68	69	70
71	72	73	74	75	76	77	78	79	80
81	82	83	84	85	86	87	88	89	90
91	92	93	94	95	96	97	98	99	100

Questions to ponder after you have played a few games:

1. Suppose that 28 and 9 are chosen as the initial numbers, like in Janes and Joe's game. Can Jane and Joe ever mark a number that is more than 28?

2. Let's say that the two initial numbers are both even. What can you say about the numbers that get marked in the game?

3. Suppose that the two initial numbers are both multiples of 5, such as 55 and 30. What can you say about the numbers that get marked in the game?

4. Can you mark off *all* of the the numbers on the 100-chart during the game, if the initial numbers are (you can try these out): **a.** 90 and 7?   **b.** 100 and 1?   **c.** 100 and 10?   **d.** 100 and 13?

100-Charts for Euclid's game or other uses

1	2	3	4	5	6	7	8	9	10
11	12	13	14	15	16	17	18	19	20
21	22	23	24	25	26	27	28	29	30
31	32	33	34	35	36	37	38	39	40
41	42	43	44	45	46	47	48	49	50
51	52	53	54	55	56	57	58	59	60
61	62	63	64	65	66	67	68	69	70
71	72	73	74	75	76	77	78	79	80
81	82	83	84	85	86	87	88	89	90
91	92	93	94	95	96	97	98	99	100

1	2	3	4	5	6	7	8	9	10
11	12	13	14	15	16	17	18	19	20
21	22	23	24	25	26	27	28	29	30
31	32	33	34	35	36	37	38	39	40
41	42	43	44	45	46	47	48	49	50
51	52	53	54	55	56	57	58	59	60
61	62	63	64	65	66	67	68	69	70
71	72	73	74	75	76	77	78	79	80
81	82	83	84	85	86	87	88	89	90
91	92	93	94	95	96	97	98	99	100

1	2	3	4	5	6	7	8	9	10
11	12	13	14	15	16	17	18	19	20
21	22	23	24	25	26	27	28	29	30
31	32	33	34	35	36	37	38	39	40
41	42	43	44	45	46	47	48	49	50
51	52	53	54	55	56	57	58	59	60
61	62	63	64	65	66	67	68	69	70
71	72	73	74	75	76	77	78	79	80
81	82	83	84	85	86	87	88	89	90
91	92	93	94	95	96	97	98	99	100

1	2	3	4	5	6	7	8	9	10
11	12	13	14	15	16	17	18	19	20
21	22	23	24	25	26	27	28	29	30
31	32	33	34	35	36	37	38	39	40
41	42	43	44	45	46	47	48	49	50
51	52	53	54	55	56	57	58	59	60
61	62	63	64	65	66	67	68	69	70
71	72	73	74	75	76	77	78	79	80
81	82	83	84	85	86	87	88	89	90
91	92	93	94	95	96	97	98	99	100

1	2	3	4	5	6	7	8	9	10
11	12	13	14	15	16	17	18	19	20
21	22	23	24	25	26	27	28	29	30
31	32	33	34	35	36	37	38	39	40
41	42	43	44	45	46	47	48	49	50
51	52	53	54	55	56	57	58	59	60
61	62	63	64	65	66	67	68	69	70
71	72	73	74	75	76	77	78	79	80
81	82	83	84	85	86	87	88	89	90
91	92	93	94	95	96	97	98	99	100

1	2	3	4	5	6	7	8	9	10
11	12	13	14	15	16	17	18	19	20
21	22	23	24	25	26	27	28	29	30
31	32	33	34	35	36	37	38	39	40
41	42	43	44	45	46	47	48	49	50
51	52	53	54	55	56	57	58	59	60
61	62	63	64	65	66	67	68	69	70
71	72	73	74	75	76	77	78	79	80
81	82	83	84	85	86	87	88	89	90
91	92	93	94	95	96	97	98	99	100

Mixed Review Chapter 8

1. Under each number in the chart, write its DOUBLE. Notice what pattern it makes!

8	9	10	11	12	13	14	15	16	17

2. Solve. Use the chart above.
    a. Two girls shared evenly 30 marbles. How many did each get?

    b. A bag of potatoes weighs 28 kg. The family ate half of it.
      How many kilograms of potatoes are left?

    c. Katy had $60. She spent half of it to buy a gift.
      Then, Katy bought a toy for $9.
      How many dollars does Katy have now?

    d. Mom used up half of the apples she had to make a pie.
      Now she has 8 apples. How many did she have to start with?

3. Subtract whole hundreds and whole tens.

a.	b.	c.
$239 - 100 =$ _____	$871 - 400 =$ _____	$704 - 500 =$ _____
d.	**e.**	**f.**
$376 - 40 =$ _____	$781 - 20 =$ _____	$1000 - 50 =$ _____

4. **a.** Circle all the months in this list that have 31 days.

January February March April May June July August September October November December

  b. Circle all the months in this list that have 30 days.

January February March April May June July August September October November December

  c. Which month didn't get circled either time? _____

    How many days does it have? _____

122

5. Color. Then compare and write < , > , or = . Which is more "pie" to eat?

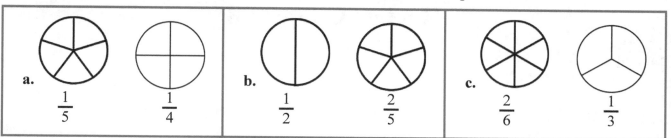

a. $\frac{1}{5}$ $\frac{1}{4}$

b. $\frac{1}{2}$ $\frac{2}{5}$

c. $\frac{2}{6}$ $\frac{1}{3}$

6. Find out what number the triangle means. Also explain how you do it!

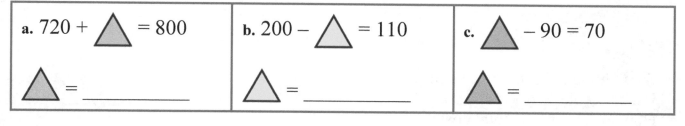

a. $720 + \triangle = 800$

$\triangle = $ _____

b. $200 - \triangle = 110$

$\triangle = $ _____

c. $\triangle - 90 = 70$

$\triangle = $ _____

7. Write the time using the wordings "past" or "till", and using numbers.

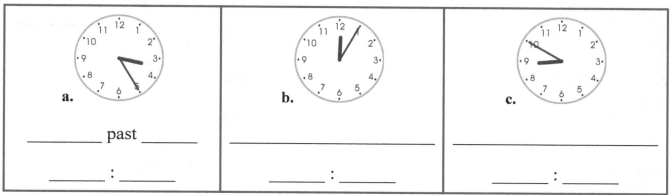

a. _____ past _____

_____ : _____

b. _____

_____ : _____

c. _____

_____ : _____

8. Measure many different erasers to the nearest whole centimeter. Then make a line plot. This means that you mark an "x" for each eraser above the number line. For example, see the lesson "Some More Measuring" in chapter 7.

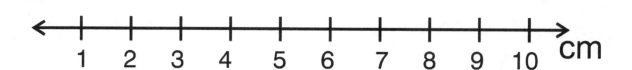

1   2   3   4   5   6   7   8   9   10   cm

Review Chapter 8

1. Add.

a.
```
  2 1 5
+ 4 7 7
```

b.
```
  1 9 2
+ 2 2 5
```

c.
```
  3 0 3
  1 2 8
+ 2 8 7
```

d.
```
  4 0 9
  2 1 9
+ 1 3 6
```

2. Sarah bought three bicycles for her children.
   Each bicycle cost $154.
   How much was the total cost?

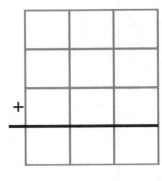

3. Add mentally. THINK of the new hundred you might get
   from adding the tens.

a.	b.	c.
80 + 40 = _____	90 + 90 = _____	690 + 50 = _____
780 + 40 = _____	240 + 50 = _____	470 + 80 = _____

4. Find how many feet it is if you walk all
   of the way around this rectangle.

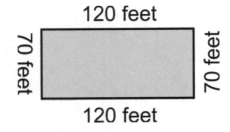

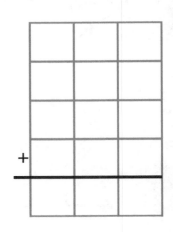

5. Subtract. Regroup if necessary. Check each subtraction by
   adding your answer and the number you subtracted.

a.	b.
$\begin{array}{r} 8\ 8 \\ -\ 5\ 4 \\ \hline \end{array}$ $\begin{array}{r} +\ 5\ 4 \\ \hline \end{array}$	$\begin{array}{r} 6\ 3 \\ -\ 4\ 8 \\ \hline \end{array}$ $\begin{array}{r} + \\ \hline \end{array}$
c.	d.
$\begin{array}{r} 8\ 4 \\ -\ 4\ 9 \\ \hline \end{array}$ $\begin{array}{r} + \\ \hline \end{array}$	$\begin{array}{r} 8\ 8\ 2 \\ -\ 1\ 5\ 9 \\ \hline \end{array}$ $\begin{array}{r} + \\ \hline \end{array}$
e.	f.
$\begin{array}{r} 5\ 5\ 6 \\ -\ 3\ 9\ 1 \\ \hline \end{array}$ $\begin{array}{r} + \\ \hline \end{array}$	$\begin{array}{r} 5\ 5\ 0 \\ -\ 2\ 4\ 6 \\ \hline \end{array}$ $\begin{array}{r} + \\ \hline \end{array}$

6. Subtract using mental math methods.

a. $15 - 7 =$ _____	b. $13 - 5 =$ _____	c. $82 - 77 =$ _____
$55 - 7 =$ _____	$93 - 5 =$ _____	$45 - 41 =$ _____
d. $80 - 71 =$ _____	e. $56 - 40 =$ _____	f. $78 - 35 =$ _____
$100 - 95 =$ _____	$56 - 43 =$ _____	$33 - 4 =$ _____

7. Find what numbers are missing.

a.
$\begin{array}{r} 2\ \square\ 4 \\ +\ 4\ 7\ 7 \\ \hline 7\ 3\ 1 \end{array}$

b.
$\begin{array}{r} 5\ \square\ 9 \\ +\ \square\ 2\ 5 \\ \hline 9\ 1\ 4 \end{array}$

c.
$\begin{array}{r} 2\ 0\ \square \\ +\ 6\ \square\ 6 \\ \hline 8\ 9\ 2 \end{array}$

d.
$\begin{array}{r} 6\ 8\ \square \\ +\ \square\ 1\ 9 \\ \hline 9\ 0\ 0 \end{array}$

8. Solve.

a. Some people are riding on the bus. At the bus stop, 13 people get on. Now there are 52 people on the bus. How many were there originally?

b. Molly has 23 stuffed toys that she likes, and 16 that she does not like.

How many stuffed toys does Molly have?

c. Molly gave the 16 toys she does not like to her sister Annie. Now, Annie has 33 toys.

How many toys did Annie have before?

d. Jessica had 465 points in a computer game. She played and got 145 more points. Then she also got a 90-point bonus! How many points does Jessica have now?

e. Olivia did 26 jumping jacks, which was 14 fewer jumping jacks than what her brother Aaron did. How many jumping jacks did Aaron do?

9. a. Fill in the table with how many points the children got in the game.

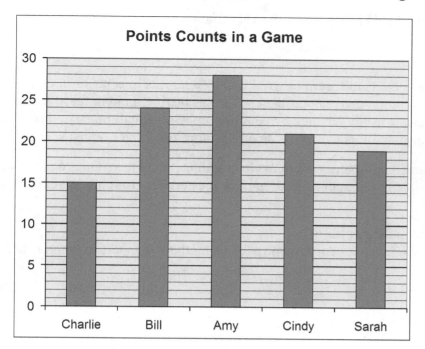

CHILD	POINTS
Charlie	15
Bill	
Amy	
Cindy	
Sarah	

b. How many fewer points did Bill get than Amy?

c. How many more points did Cindy get than Charlie?

Can you place numbers from 1 through 12 into the circles so that the sum of each connecting line is 26?

Hint: The numbers that go in the top corners are 7 and 6, and the numbers that go in the bottom corners are 5 and 8.

Puzzle Corner

127

Chapter 9: Money
Introduction

In chapter 9, children count coins and bills, and learn to write money amounts in cents or in dollars. We also practice finding change, starting with very easy problems, such as buying an item for 40¢ and paying with $1. Another skill to learn is to find change by counting up. Only small money amounts are used. If you like, you can use real or play money, and set up a play store for these exercises.

The last topic of the chapter is adding small money amounts in columns (using the standard paper-and-pencil method for addition). This topic requires that children have mastered regrouping in addition as studied in chapter 8.

You can make free worksheets for counting coins at
https://www.homeschoolmath.net/worksheets/money.php, or using the worksheet generator that comes with the curriculum.

The Lessons

Helpful Resources on the Internet

Use these free online resources to supplement the "bookwork" as you see fit.

You can also access this list of links at https://links.mathmammoth.com/gr2ch9

MathPup Truck Money
Drop the right amount of coins into the truck to make the target amount, and then drive the truck to the house.
https://www.mathnook.com/math/mathpup-truck-money.html

US Money Worksheets
Count common US coins or bills. You can choose which coins/bills will be used, and how many coins/bills are shown at most. Other currencies (Euro, Canadian, Australian, British, and South African) are available at www.homeschoolmath.net/worksheets
https://www.homeschoolmath.net/worksheets/money.php

Counting Money — Online Practice
Practice counting coins with this interactive online activity.
https://cutt.ly/count-money-practice

Fruit Splat Coins 2

Click on the fruit that shows the amount of money that corresponds with the coins shown. You can choose which coins to practice.

https://www.sheppardsoftware.com/math/money/coins-game-2/

Counting Money from Math Nook

Click on the denominations in the cash drawer so that they add up to the correct answer.

https://www.mathnook.com/math/countingmoneyint.html

Fruit Splat Dollars and Cents

Click on the fruit that shows the correct amount of money in dollars and cents.

https://www.sheppardsoftware.com/math/money/dollars-cents-game/

Addition of Money Values Quiz

Practice adding amounts of money with this short online quiz.

https://www.fractions4kids.com/addition-of-money-values-usd-math-quiz-for-kids/

Dolphin Feed

Click on coins to add up to the correct amount of money and feed the dolphin a fish.

https://www.abcya.com/games/money_counting

Change Maker

Determine how many of each denomination you need to make the exact change. Good and clear pictures! Playable in US, Canadian, Mexican, UK, or Australian money.

https://www.funbrain.com/games/change-maker

Cash Out

Give the correct change by clicking on the bills and coins.

https://mrnussbaum.com/cash-out-online-game

Quiz

A 10-question quiz on making change.

https://www.thatquiz.org/tq-a/?-j41-l8-p0

Coins and Medals from U.S. Mint

Learn about the history and see pictures of the circulating coins, commemorative coins, Native American $1 Coin Program, and the Presidential $1 Coin Program. Learn also how coins are made and take a virtual tour around the mint.

https://www.usmint.gov/learn/kids

Counting Coins Review

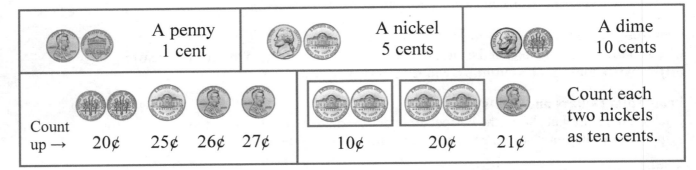

	A penny 1 cent			A nickel 5 cents			A dime 10 cents	

Count up → 20¢ 25¢ 26¢ 27¢   10¢ 20¢ 21¢   Count each two nickels as ten cents.

1. Count pennies, nickels, and dimes. Write the amount in cents.

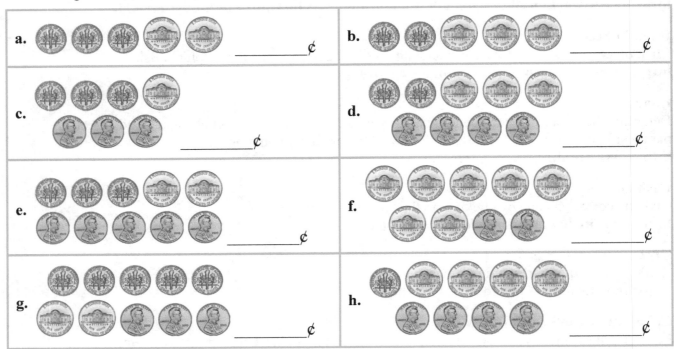

a. _____¢

b. _____¢

c. _____¢

d. _____¢

e. _____¢

f. _____¢

g. _____¢

h. _____¢

2. Make these money amounts. Use either real money, or draw.

a. 24¢	b. 17¢
c. 32¢	d. 39¢

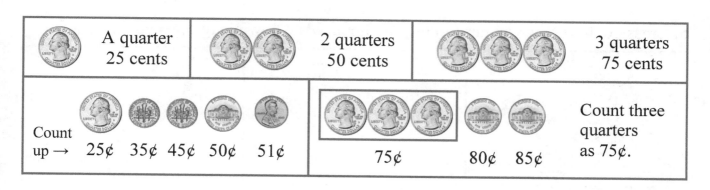

3. Count pennies, nickels, dimes, *and* quarters. Write the amount in cents.

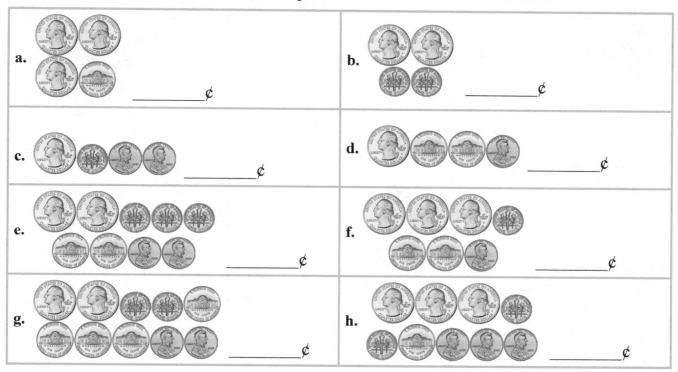

a. _____ ¢

b. _____ ¢

c. _____ ¢

d. _____ ¢

e. _____ ¢

f. _____ ¢

g. _____ ¢

h. _____ ¢

4. Make these money amounts using at least one quarter with real money,
   or you can draw coins to illustrate.

a. 26¢	b. 40¢
c. 52¢	d. 77¢

5. Cross out the coins you need to buy the item. Write how many cents you have left.

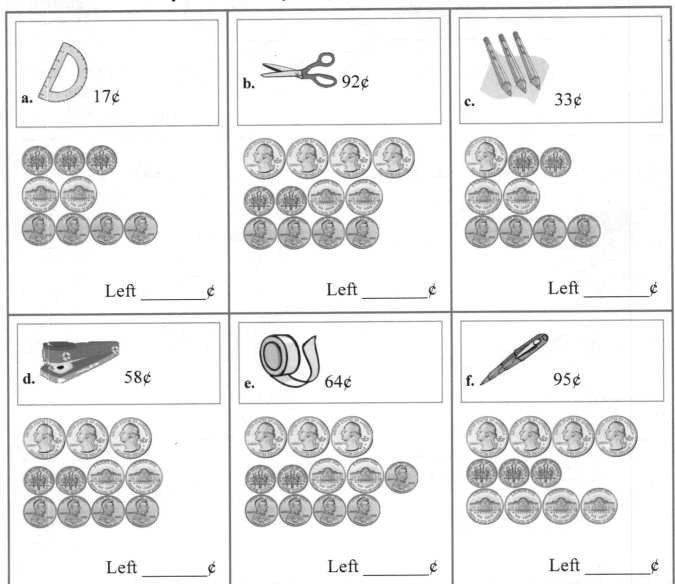

a. 17¢

Left _____ ¢

b. 92¢

Left _____ ¢

c. 33¢

Left _____ ¢

d. 58¢

Left _____ ¢

e. 64¢

Left _____ ¢

f. 95¢

Left _____ ¢

6. How much is the total if you have:

a. a nickel and three pennies _____ ¢	**b.** three dimes and three nickels _____ ¢
c. four nickels and four dimes _____ ¢	**d.** three quarters and a dime _____ ¢
e. three quarters, two dimes, a penny _____ ¢	**f.** a quarter, a dime, six pennies _____ ¢

Often you have several ways to make a given amount. For example:

 = 54¢, but also  = 54¢.

Are there any other ways to do it?

7. Find two ways to make these amounts. Use either real money, or draw the coins.

a. 36¢ - one way	b. 36¢ - another way
c. 43¢ - one way	d. 43¢ - another way
e. 88¢ - one way	f. 88¢ - another way

8. $1 means 1 dollar, which is 100 cents. How much more is needed to make $1?

a.	b.	c.
92¢ + _____ ¢ = 100¢	70¢ + _____ ¢ = $1	40¢ + _____ ¢ = $1
80¢ + _____ ¢ = $1	74¢ + _____ ¢ = $1	33¢ + _____ ¢ = $1
79¢ + _____ ¢ = $1	64¢ + _____ ¢ = $1	45¢ + _____ ¢ = $1
50¢ + _____ ¢ = $1	58¢ + _____ ¢ = $1	31¢ + _____ ¢ = $1

Change

When you buy something in a store, you often do not have the exact amount of money to pay for it. Instead, you give the clerk *more* money than what the item costs. The clerk then gives you some money back. This is called your *change*.

A pen costs 40¢. You don't have the coins to make exactly 40¢, so you give the clerk 50¢. That is 10¢ too much! But then the clerk gives you back 10¢ — your change.

You give: **Your change:**

50¢   10¢

Price: 40¢

The clerk gives you back the *difference* between the price and what you paid.

In each problem below, find the change you get back. Think of the DIFFERENCE between the price and what you pay. Or, think how many cents you paid "too much." That will be your change.

You can set up a "play store" to do these problems, using real money, one person as a clerk, and one person as a customer.

1. Write how many cents you give, and how many cents is your change.

a.   You give: Your change:

Price: 20¢   _____¢ _____¢

b.   You give: Your change:

Price: 30¢   _____¢ _____¢

c.   You give: Your change:

Price: 35¢   _____¢ _____¢

d.   You give: Your change:

Price: 17¢   _____¢ _____¢

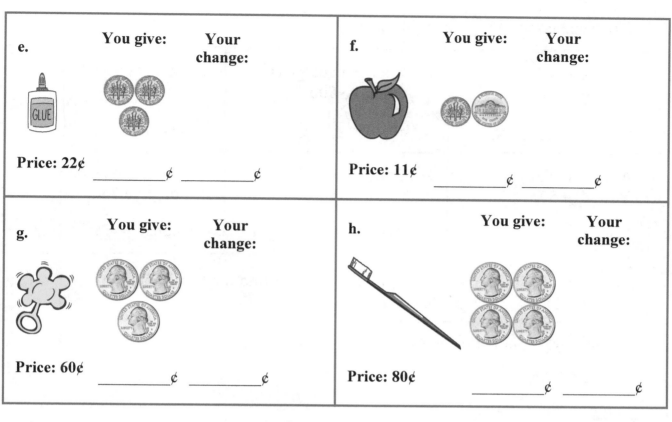

e. You give: Your change:

GLUE

Price: 22¢ _____¢ _____¢

f. You give: Your change:

Price: 11¢ _____¢ _____¢

g. You give: Your change:

Price: 60¢ _____¢ _____¢

h. You give: Your change:

Price: 80¢ _____¢ _____¢

2. Circle the coins you use to pay. Write how many cents your change is.

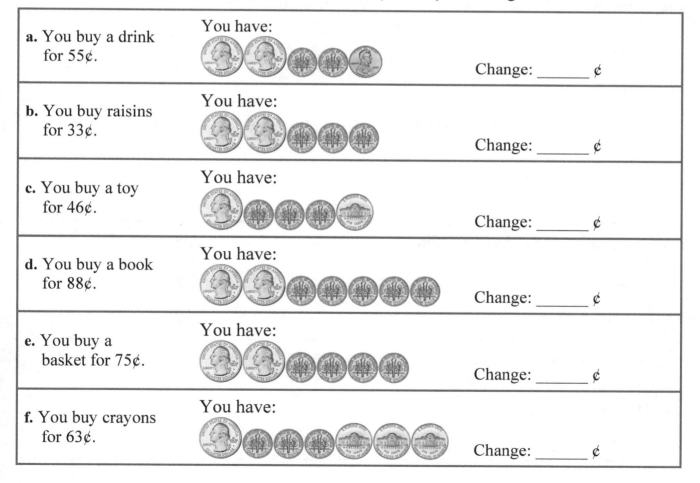

a. You buy a drink for 55¢.

You have:

Change: _____ ¢

b. You buy raisins for 33¢.

You have:

Change: _____ ¢

c. You buy a toy for 46¢.

You have:

Change: _____ ¢

d. You buy a book for 88¢.

You have:

Change: _____ ¢

e. You buy a basket for 75¢.

You have:

Change: _____ ¢

f. You buy crayons for 63¢.

You have:

Change: _____ ¢

3. Practice some more! Figure out the change.

a. Paper costs 70¢. You give $1. Change: _____ ¢	**b.** A banana costs 41¢. You give 50¢. Change: _____ ¢	**c.** A book costs 94¢. You give $1. Change: _____ ¢
d. A toy costs 20¢. You give 50¢. Change: _____ ¢	**e.** A drink costs 70¢. You give $1. Change: _____ ¢	**f.** A towel costs 62¢. You give 75¢. Change: _____ ¢

4. Now you buy many items. First add their prices to find the total. Then find the change. Draw the coins that could be your change.

a. A magazine costs 20¢. You buy three of them. You give $1.

Total cost: 60¢

Change: 40¢

b. A toy costs 15¢ and another toy 20¢. You give 50¢.

Total cost: _____ ¢

Change: _____ ¢

c. A lollipop costs 8¢. You buy two of them. You give 20¢.

Total cost: _____ ¢

Change: _____ ¢

d. A pencil costs 5¢. You buy four of them. You give 25¢.

Total cost: _____ ¢

Change: _____ ¢

e. An eraser costs 35¢ and a pencil 10¢. You give 50¢.

Total cost: _____ ¢

Change: _____ ¢

Dollars

 This is one dollar.
It is worth 100 cents.

$1 or $1.00

 = $1.20

 This is a five-dollar bill.
It is worth 500 cents.

$5 or $5.00

 =$5.26

First write the dollars, then a point, then the cents. Use the "$" symbol in front of dollar amounts. Do not use the ¢ symbol.

1. How much money? Write the amount.

a. $_____

b. $_____

c. $_____

d. $_____

e. $_____

f. $_____

g. $_____

h. $_____

2. Write the dollar amount.

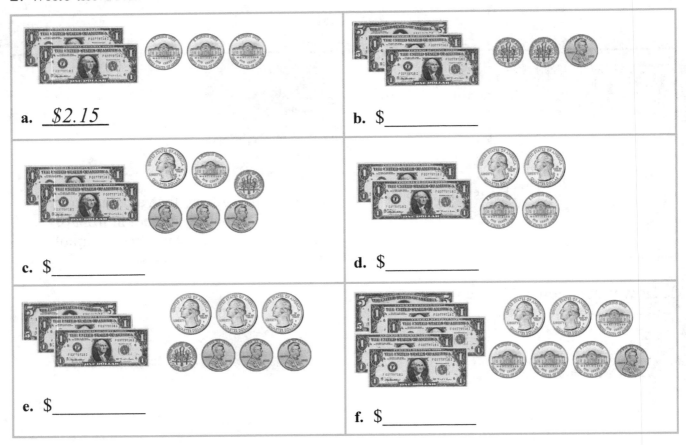

a. $2.15

b. $_____

c. $_____

d. $_____

e. $_____

f. $_____

If there are no dollars, then put a zero in the dollars place.

35¢ or $0.35

1¢ or $0.01

6¢ or $0.06

3. Write the amount using the dollar symbol and a decimal point.

a.

$_____

b.

$_____

c.

$_____

d.

$_____

e.

$_____

f.

$_____

Sometimes you have more than 100 cents. That means you have more than 1 dollar, because 1 dollar is 100 cents.

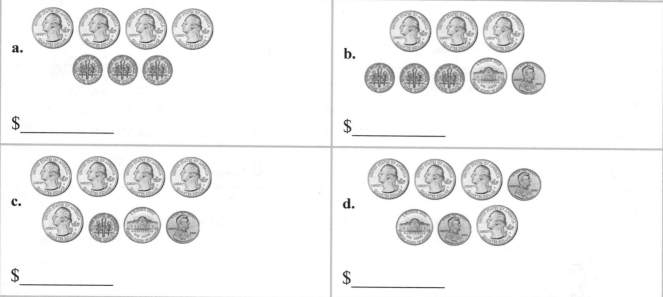

100¢ or $1.00   105¢ or $1.05   121¢ or $1.21

4. Write the amount in <u>dollars</u>.

a. $_____	**b.** $_____
c. $_____	**d.** $_____

5. Draw bills and coins for these amounts.

a. $1.32	**b.** $2.06
c. $2.54	**d.** $3.80

Counting Change

When you buy an item, you might not have the exact coins and bills for the amount it costs. You can then pay with a bigger bill, and get back some change.

To give change, or to check the change you are given, you can <u>count up</u> from *the price* of the item until you reach the amount the customer gives.

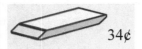 34¢

Customer gives $1

Count up from the price →

35¢   40¢   50¢   75¢   100¢

The change is these coins. The change is 66¢.

Notice: you first count up from 34¢ to 40¢ — to the next ten-cent amount.

 68¢

Customer gives $1

Count up from the price →

69¢   70¢   80¢   90¢   100¢

The change is these coins. The change is 32¢.

Notice: you first count up from 68¢ to 70¢ — to the next ten-cent amount.

1. Draw the coins for the change. Count up! You can also do this with real money.

a. 78¢ Customer gives $1	Change: _____
b. 65¢ Customer gives $1	Change: _____
c. 47¢ Customer gives $1	Change: _____
d. 52¢ Customer gives $1	Change: _____

2. Draw the coins for the change.

a.  $1.15

Customer gives $2

Change: _____

b.  $2.30

Customer gives $2.50

Change: _____

c.  $1.78

Customer gives $2

Change: _____

d. 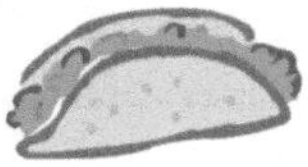 $2.32

Customer gives $3

Change: _____

3. Find the change. You can draw coins or use real money to help.

a. A toy: $1.44	b. A drink: $0.88
Customer gives $1.50	Customer gives $1
Change $_____	Change $_____
c. Coffee: $0.97	d. A pencil set: $1.55
Customer gives $1.00	Customer gives $1.75
Change $_____	Change $_____
e. A book: $3.25	f. A postcard: $0.35
Customer gives $4	Customer gives $0.50
Change $_____	Change $_____

Adding Money Amounts

You can add money amounts in columns.

Make sure the decimal points are aligned.

Add the point to the answer in the same place.

Regrouping happens the same way as if there was no decimal point.

Align the decimal points!

$$\begin{array}{r} \$1.7\ 8 \\ +\ \ 2.2\ 0 \\ \hline \$3.9\ 8 \end{array}$$

↓ Align the decimal points!
↑ Add a decimal point to the answer.

Align the decimal points! 1

$$\begin{array}{r} \$0.5\ 8 \\ +\ \ 2.2\ 6 \\ \hline \$2.8\ 4 \end{array}$$

↑ Add a decimal point to the answer.

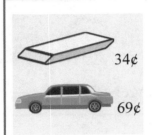

34¢

69¢

1 1
$$\begin{array}{r} \$0.3\ 4 \\ +\ \ 0.6\ 9 \\ \hline \$1.0\ 3 \end{array}$$

Total cost $1.03.

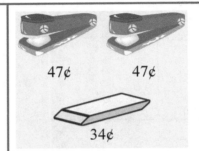

47¢   47¢

34¢

1 1
$$\begin{array}{r} \$0.4\ 7 \\ 0.4\ 7 \\ +\ \ 0.3\ 4 \\ \hline \$1.2\ 8 \end{array}$$

Total cost $1.28.

1. Add.   **a.** $0.29 + $0.56   **b.** $1.41 + $0.09   **c.** $0.77 + $2.24 + $1.80

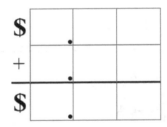   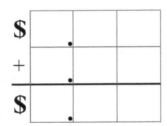   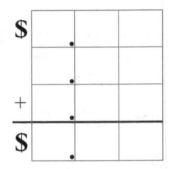

2. Find the total cost of buying the things listed.

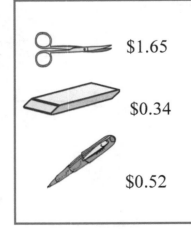

$1.65

$0.34

$0.52

a. scissors and a pen

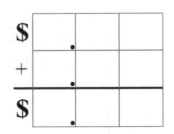

b. two erasers and a pen

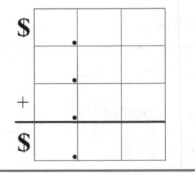

| Cafeteria Menu | $0.88 |  $1.52 |  $2.20 | $2.75 | $1.05 | $0.62 |

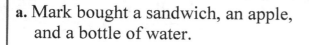

3. Find the total cost in each case.

a. Mark bought a sandwich, an apple, and a bottle of water.

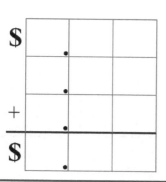

b. Judy bought hot chocolate and a slice of pizza.

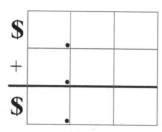

c. Edward bought soup, a sandwich, and hot chocolate.

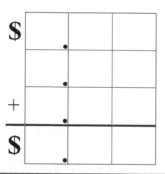

d. What would you buy if you were at the cafeteria? Find the total cost.

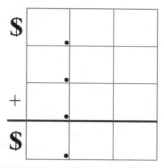

4. Find the change for the people in the previous exercise.

a. Mark paid with $5.

b. Judy paid with $4.

c. Edward paid with $5.

Mixed Review Chapter 9

1. Write the numbers in columns and add.

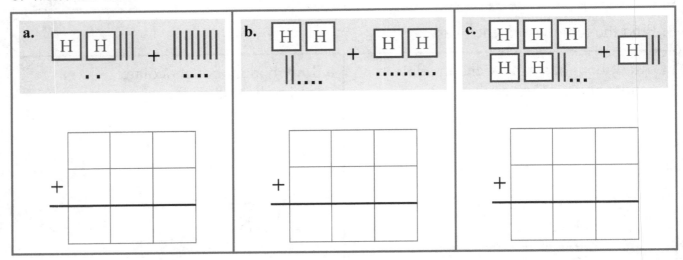

2. Solve.

a. Mary has 78 marbles. Her brother had 13 fewer marbles than her. How many marbles do the children have together?

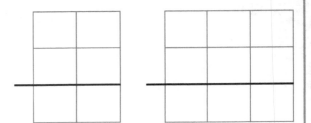

b. Mom had $250 with her when she went shopping. She bought groceries for $120, and gasoline for $50. How much money does she have left now?

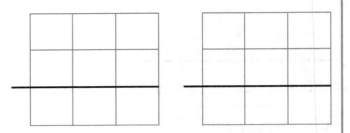

c. Pablo has read 141 pages of a book that has 213 pages. How many pages does he have left to read?

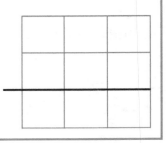

3. Subtract. Regroup if necessary. Check each subtraction by *adding your answer and the number you subtracted.*

a.		b.	
$\begin{array}{r} 9\ 3 \\ -\ 2\ 8 \\ \hline \end{array}$	$\begin{array}{r} +\ 2\ 8 \\ \hline \end{array}$	$\begin{array}{r} 5\ 2\ 8 \\ -\ 2\ 4\ 5 \\ \hline \end{array}$	$\begin{array}{r} + \\ \hline \end{array}$

4. Measure the sides of this triangle BOTH in inches, to the nearest half-inch, and in centimeters, to the nearest centimeter. Write your results in the table.

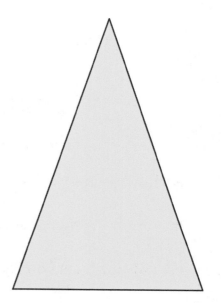

Triangle	in inches	in centimeters
Side 1	in.	cm
Side 2	in.	cm
Side 3	in.	cm

5. The pictograph shows how many fish the family members caught when they went fishing.

Dad	🐟🐟🐟🐟🐟🐟
Mom	🐟🐟🐟🐟🐟🐟🐟🐟
Amy	🐟🐟🐟🐟
Chris	🐟🐟🐟🐟🐟🐟🐟🐟🐟🐟🐟

a. Who caught the most fish?

b. How many more fish did Chris catch than Dad?

c. How many fewer fish did Amy catch than Mom?

d. How many did Amy and Chris catch together?

6. The bar graph shows how many toy cars some kids have. Chloe has 14 cars.
   Draw a bar for her in the graph.

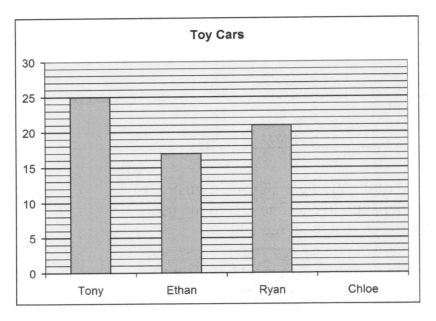

a. How many cars does Ethan have?

b. How many more cars does Tony have than Ethan?

c. How many cars do Ryan and Chloe have together?

d. If Ethan gives Ryan 5 cars, will Ryan then have more than Tony?

Puzzle Corner

Can you place numbers from 1 through 9 into the circles so that the sum of each side of the triangle is 20?

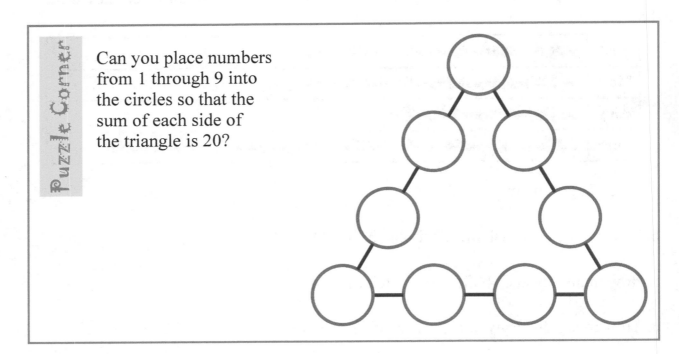

146

Review Chapter 9

1. How much is the total if you have:

a. a quarter, a nickel and three pennies	**b.** three dimes and four nickels
_____ ¢	_____ ¢

2. Make these money amounts. Use real money or draw. Use at least one quarter.

a. 28¢	**b.** 93¢

3. Write the **dollar** amount.

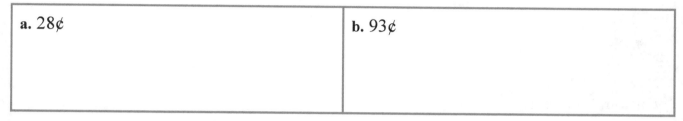

a. $ _____   b. $ _____

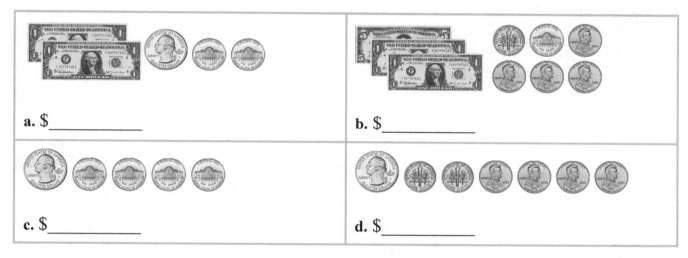

c. $ _____   d. $ _____

4. Write how many cents you give, and how many cents is your change.

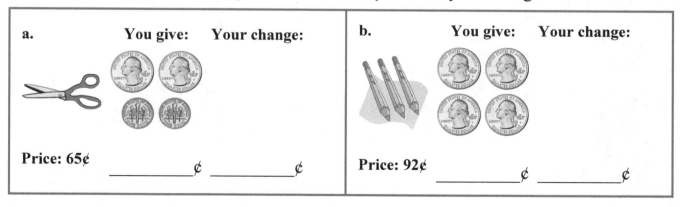

a.   **You give:**   **Your change:**

Price: 65¢   _____ ¢   _____ ¢

b.   **You give:**   **Your change:**

Price: 92¢   _____ ¢   _____ ¢

5. Count up to find the change. Draw the coins for the change.

a.  $2.15

Customer gives $3   Change: _____

b.  $1.59

Customer gives $2   Change: _____

c.  $4.85

Customer gives $5   Change: _____

6. Lily has $1.26. Alex has two dimes, two quarters,
   and seven pennies in his piggy bank.
   How much money does Alex have?

   How much money do the children have together?

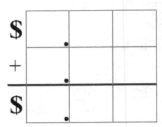

7. Find the total cost of buying the things listed.

$0.98

$1.65

$0.78

a. a yogurt and an apple

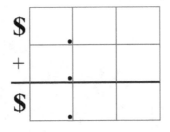

b. two yogurts and a sandwich

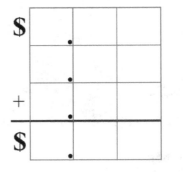

Chapter 10: Exploring Multiplication
Introduction

The last chapter of *Math Mammoth Grade 2* covers the concept of multiplication, its connection with repeated addition, and some easy multiplication practice.

The lessons here are self-explanatory. The student first learns the meaning of multiplication as "many times the same size group". Then we practice writing multiplication as repeated addition and vice versa. Number-line jumps are another way to illustrate multiplication.

The actual study and memorization of the multiplication tables is in the third grade. However, you can certainly help your child to notice the patterns in the easy tables of 2, 5, and 10, and encourage their memorization.

If the time allows and the child is receptive, now you can study multiplication tables even further.

The Lessons

Helpful Resources on the Internet

Use these free online resources to supplement the "bookwork" as you see fit.

You can also access this list of links at **https://l.mathmammoth.com/gr2ch10**

Scan me

Relate Repeated Addition to Multiplication
Reinforce your knowledge of the connection between repeated addition and multiplication with this interactive multiple-choice exercise.
https://www.khanacademy.org/math/cc-third-grade-math/intro-to-multiplication/imp-multiplication-intro/e/relate-repeated-addition-to-multiplication

Multiplication Worksheets: Skip Count on a Number Line
Use these free printable worksheets for extra practice.
https://www.k5learning.com/free-math-worksheets/third-grade-3/multiplication/number-line

Skip Count Advanced

Choose the number to skip count by. Then try to hit the fruit with the correct number.

https://www.sheppardsoftware.com/math/early-math/skip-count-advanced-fruit-splat-game/

Online Skip Counting Games

A collection of games for skip-counting.

https://www.free-training-tutorial.com/skip-counting-games.html

Represent Multiplication on the Number Line

Practice using a number line to solve multiplication problems in this interactive online exercise.

https://www.khanacademy.org/math/arithmetic/arith-review-multiply-divide/arith-review-mult-intro/e/number_line

Math Dice Game for Addition and Multiplication

Instructions for three simple games with dice; one to learn the concept of multiplication, another to practice the times tables, and one more for addition facts.

http://www.teachingwithtlc.blogspot.com/2007/09/math-dice-games-for-addition-and.html

Multiplication Picnic

Some children are having a picnic. Multiply to find out how much food they have.

https://games.forkids.education/picnic-multiplication/

Balloon Pop Math - Multiplication

Solve the problems and pop the balloons in order - from the smallest to the biggest answer. Choose "Level 1".

https://www.sheppardsoftware.com/math/multiplication/balloon-pop/

Town Creator

Answer the problems correctly to add houses, trees, cars, and more to your town and make it more beautiful!

https://www.free-training-tutorial.com/times-tables/towncreator/tc-multiplication.html

Many Times the Same Group

1. Write.

a. 2 times the word "CAT"	**b.** 3 times the word "ME"	**c.** 5 times the word "YOU"
d. 0 times the word "FROG"	**e.** 4 times the word "SCHOOL"	**f.** 1 time the word "HERE"

2. Draw groups of balls.

a. 2 times a group of 3 balls	**b.** 3 times a group of 5 balls	**c.** 1 time a group of 7 balls
d. 4 times a group of 1 ball	**e.** 0 times a group of 2 balls	**f.** 3 times a group of 3 balls
g. 0 times a group of 8 balls	**h.** 4 times a group of 0 balls	**i.** 5 times a group of 2 balls

3. Fill in the missing parts.

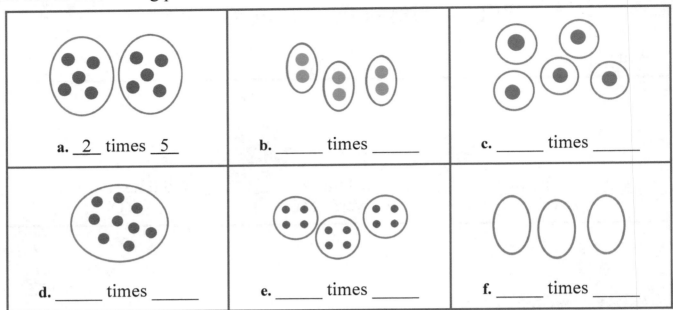

a. __2__ times __5__

b. _____ times _____

c. _____ times _____

d. _____ times _____

e. _____ times _____

f. _____ times _____

5 × 3	2 × 7
This means "5 times a group of 3."	This means "2 times a group of 7."
It is called **multiplication**.	You *multiply* 2 times 7.

4. Now it is your turn to draw! Notice also the symbol × which is read "times."

a. 2 times 4 2 × 4	b. 3 times 6 3 × 6	c. 1 times 7 1 × 7
d. 6 times 1 6 × 1	e. 4 times 0 4 × 0	f. 2 times 2 2 × 2

5. Write the multiplication sentence. Write the total after the " = " sign.

a.

2 × 6 = 12

b.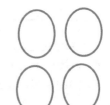

_____ × _____ = _____

c.

_____ × _____ = _____

d.

_____ × _____ = _____

e.

_____ × _____ = _____

f.

_____ × _____ = _____

6. Draw the groups. Write the total.

a. 8 × 1 = _____

b. 1 × 10 = _____

c. 2 × 2 = _____

d. 5 × 2 = _____

e. 2 × 8 = _____

f. 3 × 3 = _____

Multiplication and Addition

When the same group is repeated many times, you can write an addition sentence, and a multiplication sentence.

You add the same number many times. Multiplication is repeated addition.

$$\begin{array}{r} 2 \\ 2 \\ + \ 2 \\ \hline 6 \end{array}$$

$3 \times 2 = 6$

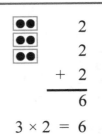

$5 + 5 + 5 = 15$

$3 \times 5 = 15$

1. Write an addition and a multiplication sentence for each problem.

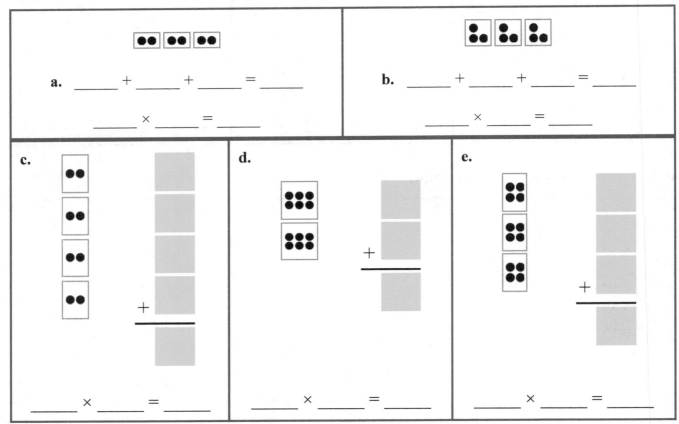

a. _____ + _____ + _____ = _____

_____ × _____ = _____

b. _____ + _____ + _____ = _____

_____ × _____ = _____

c. _____ × _____ = _____

d. _____ × _____ = _____

e. _____ × _____ = _____

2. Draw groups to match the sum. Then write a multiplication sentence.

a. $7 + 7$

_____ × _____ = _____

b. $1 + 1 + 1 + 1$

_____ × _____ = _____

c. $5 + 5 + 5$

_____ × _____ = _____

3. Fill in.

a.

_4_ groups, _2_ scissors in each.

_4_ × _2_ scissors = _____ scissors

_2_ + _2_ + ____ + ____

b.

____ groups, ____ rams in each.

_____ × _____ rams = _____ rams

_____ + _____ + _____ + _____

c.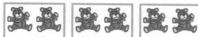

____ groups, ____ bears in each.

_____ × _____ bears = _____ bears

_____ + _____ + _____

d.

____ groups, ____ carrots in each.

_____ × _____ carrots = _____ carrots

_____ + _____

e.

____ groups, ____ books in each.

_____ × _____ books = _____ books

_____ + _____ + _____

f.

____ groups, ____ bulbs in each.

_____ × _____ bulbs = _____ bulbs

_____ + _____ + _____ + _____

g.

____ groups, ____ scissors in each.

____ × ____ scissors = _____ scissors

____ + ____ + ____ + ____ + ____

h.

____ groups, ____ rams in each.

_____ × _____ rams = _____ rams

_____ + _____

155

4. Write an addition and a multiplication sentence for each picture.

a.

___ + ___ + ___ + ___ + ___ = _____

_____ × _____ = _____

b.

___ + ___ + ___ = _____

_____ × _____ = _____

c.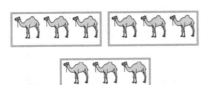

___ + ___ + ___ = _____

_____ × _____ = _____

d.

___ + ___ = _____

_____ × _____ = _____

e.

_____

_____ × _____ = _____

f.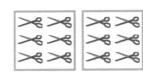

_____

_____ × _____ = _____

g.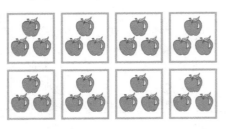

_____

_____ × _____ = _____

h.

_____

_____ × _____ = _____

5. Now it is your turn to draw. Then write the multiplication sentence.

a. Draw 3 groups of seven sticks. _____ × _____ = _____	**b.** Draw 2 groups of eight dots. _____ × _____ = _____
c. Draw 4 groups of four dots. _____ × _____ = _____	**d.** Draw 5 groups of two dots. _____ × _____ = _____
e. Draw 4 groups of two sticks. _____ × _____ = _____	**f.** Draw 10 groups of one stick. _____ × _____ = _____
g. Draw 5 groups of three sticks. _____ × _____ = _____	**h.** Draw 7 groups of two sticks. _____ × _____ = _____

Multiplying on a Number Line

Five jumps, each is two steps.

$5 \times 2 = 10$.

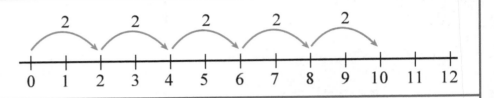

Four jumps, each is three steps.

$4 \times 3 = 12$.

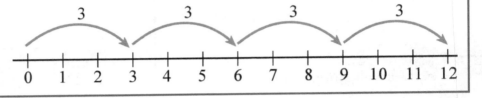

1. Write the multiplication sentence that the jumps on the number line illustrate.

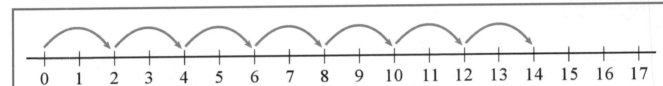

a. _____ × _____ = _____

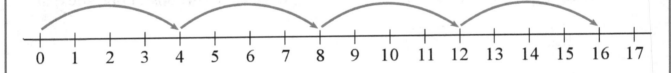

b. _____ × _____ = _____

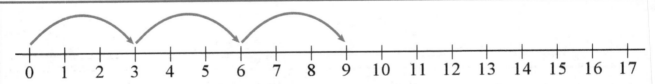

c. _____ × _____ = _____

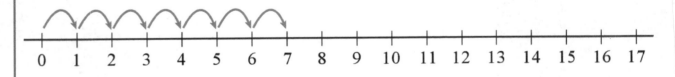

d. _____ × _____ = _____

2. Draw more "skips" of three.

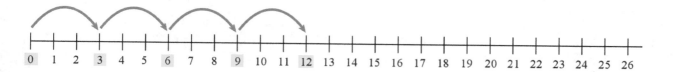

3. Multiply times 3. Use the skips above to help.

a. $5 \times 3 =$ _____	**b.** $8 \times 3 =$ _____	**c.** $6 \times 3 =$ _____	**d.** $2 \times 3 =$ _____
$4 \times 3 =$ _____	$7 \times 3 =$ _____	$3 \times 3 =$ _____	$9 \times 3 =$ _____

4. How many skips of three are needed? Use the number line above to help.

a. _____ $\times 3 = 24$	**b.** _____ $\times 3 = 18$	**c.** _____ $\times 3 = 21$	**d.** _____ $\times 3 = 6$
_____ $\times 3 = 9$	_____ $\times 3 = 15$	_____ $\times 3 = 12$	_____ $\times 3 = 3$

5. Draw more "skips" of four.

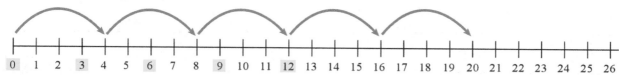

6. Multiply times 4. Use the skips above to help.

a. $2 \times 4 =$ _____	**b.** $6 \times 4 =$ _____	**c.** $8 \times 4 =$ _____	**d.** $5 \times 4 =$ _____
$4 \times 4 =$ _____	$7 \times 4 =$ _____	$3 \times 4 =$ _____	$1 \times 4 =$ _____

7. How many skips of four are needed? Use the number line above to help.

a. _____ $\times 4 = 24$	**b.** _____ $\times 4 = 0$	**c.** _____ $\times 4 = 16$	**d.** _____ $\times 4 = 20$
_____ $\times 4 = 8$	_____ $\times 4 = 12$	_____ $\times 4 = 24$	_____ $\times 4 = 4$

8. Continue and draw jumps to fit the multiplication problem.

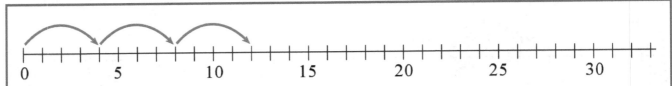

a. $6 \times 4 =$ _____

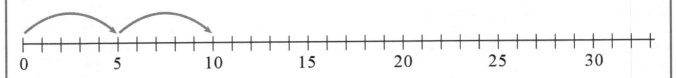

b. $5 \times 5 =$ _____

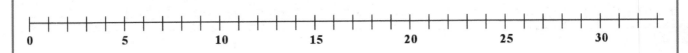

c. $6 \times 1 =$ _____

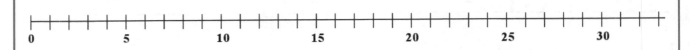

d. $9 \times 3 =$ _____

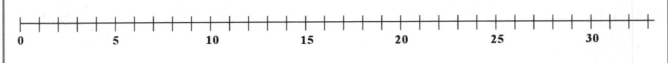

e. $3 \times 10 =$ _____

9. Multiply without a number line, if you can!

a. $3 \times 4 =$ _____	**b.** $2 \times 11 =$ _____	**c.** $4 \times 5 =$ _____	**d.** $3 \times 6 =$ _____

10. Fill in the missing number.

a. $3 \times \bigcirc \times 2 = 12$	**c.** $2 \times \bigcirc \times 2 = 24$	**e.** $2 \times \bigcirc \times 2 = 28$
b. $\bigcirc \times 3 \times 2 = 18$	**d.** $5 \times 2 \times \bigcirc = 30$	Puzzle Corner

Multiplication Practice

1. Multiply. Think of repeated addition!

a. $2 \times 3 =$ _____	**b.** $3 \times 2 =$ _____	**c.** $3 \times 10 =$ _____
$2 \times 4 =$ _____	$3 \times 3 =$ _____	$5 \times 10 =$ _____
$2 \times 5 =$ _____	$3 \times 4 =$ _____	$6 \times 10 =$ _____

2. Write a multiplication sentence from the addition sentence. Solve.

a. $11 + 11$ _____ $\times$ _____ $=$ _____	**b.** $0 + 0 + 0 + 0$ _____ $\times$ _____ $=$ _____	**c.** $10 + 10 + 10 + 10 + 10$ _____ $\times$ _____ $=$ _____
d. $1 + 1 + 1 + 1 + 1$ _____ $\times$ _____ $=$ _____	**e.** $4 + 4 + 4$ _____ $\times$ _____ $=$ _____	**f.** $20 + 20 + 20$ _____ $\times$ _____ $=$ _____
g. $300 + 300 + 300$ _____ $\times$ _____ $=$ _____	**h.** $10 + 10 + 10 + 10 + 10 + 10 + 10$ _____ $\times$ _____ $=$ _____	

3.

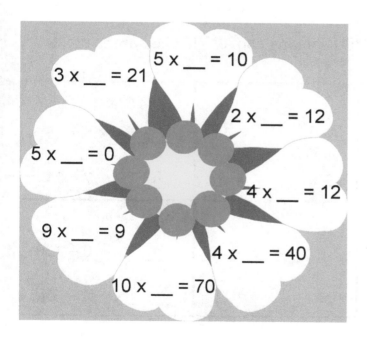

3. If the answer is...

0, color the petal yellow.
1, color the petal orange.
2, color the petal red.
3, color the petal green.
6, color the petal blue.
7, color the petal purple.
10, color the petal brown.

4. Fill in the multiplication table of 2. Count by twos.

$1 \times 2 = $ _____	$4 \times 2 = $ _____	$7 \times 2 = $ _____	$10 \times 2 = $ _____
$2 \times 2 = $ _____	$5 \times 2 = $ _____	$8 \times 2 = $ _____	$11 \times 2 = $ _____
$3 \times 2 = $ _____	$6 \times 2 = $ _____	$9 \times 2 = $ _____	$12 \times 2 = $ _____

5. Fill in the multiplication table of 5. Count by fives.

$1 \times 5 = $ _____	$4 \times 5 = $ _____	$7 \times 5 = $ _____	$10 \times 5 = $ _____
$2 \times 5 = $ _____	$5 \times 5 = $ _____	$8 \times 5 = $ _____	$11 \times 5 = $ _____
$3 \times 5 = $ _____	$6 \times 5 = $ _____	$9 \times 5 = $ _____	$12 \times 5 = $ _____

6. Fill in the multiplication table of 10. Count by tens.

$1 \times 10 = $ _____	$4 \times 10 = $ _____	$7 \times 10 = $ _____	$10 \times 10 = $ _____
$2 \times 10 = $ _____	$5 \times 10 = $ _____	$8 \times 10 = $ _____	$11 \times 10 = $ _____
$3 \times 10 = $ _____	$6 \times 10 = $ _____	$9 \times 10 = $ _____	$12 \times 10 = $ _____

7. Try to fill in the correct numbers WITHOUT looking above! Then, color the boxes with any colors you like!

a.	b.	c.	d.
$2 \times $ _____ $ = 10$	_____ $ \times 10 = 100$	$5 \times $ _____ $ = 45$	_____ $ \times 5 = 25$
$3 \times $ _____ $ = 9$	_____ $ \times 2 = 18$	$3 \times $ _____ $ = 6$	_____ $ \times 7 = 21$
e.	**f.**	**g.**	**h.**
$7 \times $ _____ $ = 14$	_____ $ \times 5 = 35$	$10 \times $ _____ $ = 60$	_____ $ \times 10 = 120$
$5 \times $ _____ $ = 20$	_____ $ \times 4 = 12$	$2 \times $ _____ $ = 16$	_____ $ \times 12 = 24$

Mixed Review Chapter 10

1. Subtract mentally.

a. 644 – 20 = _____	b. 777 – 70 = _____	c. 98 – 26 = _____
644 – 400 = _____	777 – 500 = _____	100 – 96 = _____

2. How much money? Write the amount.

a. $_____   b. $_____

3. Amy's piggy bank had 57¢. Brett's piggy bank had four quarters.

How many _cents_ does Brett have?

How many cents do the two children have
if they put their money together?

4. You buy some items. Find the total. Then find the change. Draw the coins that would
be used for your change.

a. A tennis ball costs $1.10. You give $5.

Total cost: _____

Change: _____

b. A drink costs 80¢. You buy two of them. You give $2.

Total cost: _____

Change: _____

5. Write the time using the wordings "past" or "till", and using numbers.

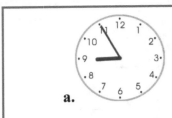

a. _____

_____ : _____

b. _____

_____ : _____

c. _____

_____ : _____

6. Write the time 5 minutes later than what the clocks show in the previous exercise.

a._____ : _____

a._____ : _____

a._____ : _____

7. Subtract. Regroup if necessary. Check each subtraction by *adding your answer and the number you subtracted.*

a.

```
  6 5 2
- 2 2 7
_____        +  _____
```

b.

```
  5 4 8
- 1 8 5
_____        +  _____
```

8. Find how many meters it is if you walk all the way around this park.

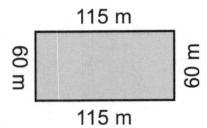

115 m

60 m

60 m

115 m

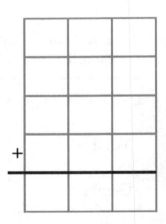

9. Find out what number the triangle means.

a. 560 + △ = 600

△ = _____

b. 400 − △ = 310

△ = _____

c. △ − 60 = 60

△ = _____

164

10. Draw rectangles containing the number of little squares asked for.
    Guess and check!

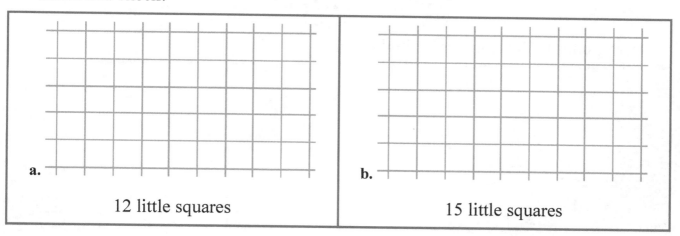

a.

12 little squares

b.

15 little squares

11. A *face* is any of the flat sides of a solid.

   a. Count how many faces a cube has. _____ faces

   What shapes are they? _____

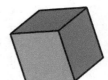

   b. Count how many faces a box has. _____ faces

   What shapes are they? _____

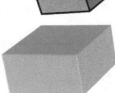

12. What shapes are these?

a.

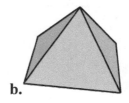

b.

_____

_____

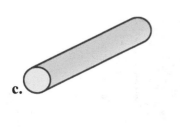

c.

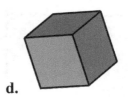

d.

_____

_____

Review Chapter 10

1. Draw groups to illustrate the multiplications.

a. $5 \times 1 =$ _____	**b.** $2 \times 10 =$ _____	**c.** $3 \times 2 =$ _____

2. Draw number-line jumps to illustrate these multiplication sentences.

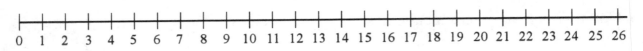

a. $3 \times 6 =$ _____

b. $4 \times 3 =$ _____

3. Write each multiplication as an addition.

a. 3×3	**b.** 4×2

4. Multiply.

a. $2 \times 3 =$ _____	**b.** $3 \times 3 =$ _____	**c.** $1 \times 3 =$ _____
$2 \times 10 =$ _____	$3 \times 20 =$ _____	$2 \times 0 =$ _____
$2 \times 20 =$ _____	$7 \times 1 =$ _____	$4 \times 5 =$ _____

5. Hannah made many math problems from the same picture. Solve the problems.

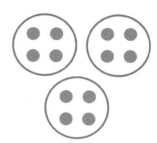

    a. $4 + 4 + 4 =$ _____   **b.** $12 - 4 =$ _____

    c. $4 + 4 =$ _____   **d.** $12 - 4 - 4 =$ _____

    e. $3 \times 4 =$ _____   **f.** $1 \times 4 =$ _____

6. Make as many math problems as you can from this picture:

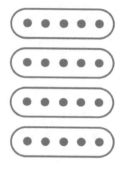

7. Solve.

    a. Katie had 5 vases. She put ten flowers in each vase.
       What is the total number of flowers in all the vases?

    b. John had 20 toy cars and Jim had 10. John gave half of his to Jim.
       Now who has more cars?

    How many more?

8. Draw a line from the problems to 10 or 50 if they are equal to 10 or 50.

$5 + 6$	$29 - 9$	2×5	$25 + 25$	$61 - 11$	5×10
$15 - 5$		$16 - 3 - 3$	$90 - 50$		$45 + 3 + 5$
$\frac{1}{2}$ of 10	**10**	0×10	$\frac{1}{2}$ of 100	**50**	1×50
		$\frac{1}{2}$ of 20			$\frac{1}{2}$ of 80
5×2			10×10		
$3 + 3 + 3$	1×5	$6 + 4$	$20 + 20 + 10$	2×20	$70 - 20$